Radiation Protection

Radiological Protection of the Environment
The Path Forward to a New Policy?

NEA Forum in Collaboration with the International Commission on Radiological Protection (ICRP)

Taormina, Sicily, Italy
12-14 February 2002

NUCLEAR ENERGY AGENCY
ORGANISATION FOR ECONOMIC CO-OPERATION AND DEVELOPMENT

ORGANISATION FOR ECONOMIC CO-OPERATION AND DEVELOPMENT

Pursuant to Article 1 of the Convention signed in Paris on 14th December 1960, and which came into force on 30th September 1961, the Organisation for Economic Co-operation and Development (OECD) shall promote policies designed:

- to achieve the highest sustainable economic growth and employment and a rising standard of living in Member countries, while maintaining financial stability, and thus to contribute to the development of the world economy;
- to contribute to sound economic expansion in Member as well as non-member countries in the process of economic development; and
- to contribute to the expansion of world trade on a multilateral, non-discriminatory basis in accordance with international obligations.

The original Member countries of the OECD are Austria, Belgium, Canada, Denmark, France, Germany, Greece, Iceland, Ireland, Italy, Luxembourg, the Netherlands, Norway, Portugal, Spain, Sweden, Switzerland, Turkey, the United Kingdom and the United States. The following countries became Members subsequently through accession at the dates indicated hereafter: Japan (28th April 1964), Finland (28th January 1969), Australia (7th June 1971), New Zealand (29th May 1973), Mexico (18th May 1994), the Czech Republic (21st December 1995), Hungary (7th May 1996), Poland (22nd November 1996), Korea (12th December 1996) and the Slovak Republic (14 December 2000). The Commission of the European Communities takes part in the work of the OECD (Article 13 of the OECD Convention).

NUCLEAR ENERGY AGENCY

The OECD Nuclear Energy Agency (NEA) was established on 1st February 1958 under the name of the OEEC European Nuclear Energy Agency. It received its present designation on 20th April 1972, when Japan became its first non-European full Member. NEA membership today consists of 28 OECD Member countries: Australia, Austria, Belgium, Canada, Czech Republic, Denmark, Finland, France, Germany, Greece, Hungary, Iceland, Ireland, Italy, Japan, Luxembourg, Mexico, the Netherlands, Norway, Portugal, Republic of Korea, Slovak Republic, Spain, Sweden, Switzerland, Turkey, the United Kingdom and the United States. The Commission of the European Communities also takes part in the work of the Agency.

The mission of the NEA is:

- to assist its Member countries in maintaining and further developing, through international co-operation, the scientific, technological and legal bases required for a safe, environmentally friendly and economical use of nuclear energy for peaceful purposes, as well as
- to provide authoritative assessments and to forge common understandings on key issues, as input to government decisions on nuclear energy policy and to broader OECD policy analyses in areas such as energy and sustainable development.

Specific areas of competence of the NEA include safety and regulation of nuclear activities, radioactive waste management, radiological protection, nuclear science, economic and technical analyses of the nuclear fuel cycle, nuclear law and liability, and public information. The NEA Data Bank provides nuclear data and computer program services for participating countries.

In these and related tasks, the NEA works in close collaboration with the International Atomic Energy Agency in Vienna, with which it has a Co-operation Agreement, as well as with other international organisations in the nuclear field.

FOREWORD

The beneficial uses of radiation in medicine, industry and energy production have contributed to the advancement of our society. To capitalise and maximise the benefits to society of activities involving radiation, governments take action to establish regulatory programmes that ensure appropriate safeguards are in place for the protection of the public, the environment, workers and patients, from the possible deleterious effects of inappropriate use or handling of sources of radiation. One of the foundations of these efforts is a thorough understanding of radiation risks, including how these risks are assessed and managed, and how these risks are addressed in a societal context.

In recent years, the member countries of the Organisation for Economic Co-operation and Development (OECD) have shown an increasing interest in identifying opportunities to enhance protection of the environment as part of their initiatives for sustainable development. One aspect of the protection of the environment of relevance to the OECD Nuclear Energy Agency (NEA) is radiological protection of the environment. This issue has gained renewed attention recently, leading to special interest within the NEA membership to contribute to the international activities being conducted to develop a rationale for radiological protection of the environment that is comprehensive and can be implemented in an efficient manner.

Radiological protection of the environment is currently being addressed by various international initiatives. The International Commission on Radiological Protection (ICRP) has launched a task group of its Main Commission to address this issue as a part of developing new recommendations. The European Commission has established the Framework for Assessment of Environmental Impact (FASSET) project. The International Atomic Energy Agency (IAEA) has established a work programme to develop safety guidance on the protection of the environment from the effects of ionising radiation, which will take account of these and other developments.

In light of the growing interest in developing an integrated approach to the management of all environmental risks, the possibility of taking a specific approach to radiological protection of the environment should be considered, and is encouraged.

The NEA therefore proposed to conduct, in close collaboration with the ICRP, a series of fora and supporting workshops on radiological protection of the environment. Within the NEA, the Committee on Radiation Protection and Public Health (CRPPH) is interested in seeing that any policy developed in this area represents international consensus and can be practically implemented, nationally as well as internationally.

Currently, three fora are foreseen: at the beginning of the development of new ICRP recommendations to provide a rationale for radiological protection of the environment, then a second forum following reflections and draft considerations by the ICRP; and the third forum following the issuance of a new ICRP recommendation.

The first NEA forum in collaboration with the ICRP entitled "Radiological Protection of the Environment, The Path Forward to a New Policy?" was held in Taormina, Sicily, Italy, 12-14

February 2002 on the kind invitation of the Italian *Agenzia Nazionale per la Protezione dell' Ambiente* (ANPA).

The list of forum participants is provided in the Annex. The members of the Forum Programme Committee were as follows:

Prof. Dr. Roger Clarke, NRPB, United Kingdom
Ms. Francis Fry, NRPB, United Kingdom
Dr. Lars-Erik Holm, SSI, Sweden
Mr. C. Rick Jones, DOE, United States
Dr. Ted Lazo, OECD/NEA
Mr. Jacques Lochard, CEPN, France

Dr. Stefan Mundigl, OECD/NEA
Dr. Roberto Ranieri, ANPA, Italy
Dr. Hans Riotte, OECD/NEA
Dr. Jan Olof Snihs, Sweden
M. Yasuhiro Yamaguchi, JAERI, Japan

The objective of this first forum was to develop together with other interested parties a sound technical basis and criteria for an ICRP Radiological Protection of the Environment Recommendation. This first meeting focused on the questions:

- How best can we enlighten the process of developing a radiological protection philosophy for the environment?

- What harm do we wish to prevent and how will we measure that harm?

- How could the systems for the radiological protection of the environment and the radiological protection of man be integrated, and are there any inherent conflicts that need to be considered?

The forum was organised in four sessions with invited speakers introducing the topics, each session followed by a panel discussion, which tried to answer the open questions:

- What problem are we trying to solve? Is there an international rationale behind the wish to protect the environment from radiation?

- Do we have enough scientific information to develop and define a broadly accepted policy?

- What are the socio-political dynamics, beyond science, that will influence policy on radiological protection of the environment?

- What are the characteristics of the process for developing a system of radiological protection of the environment?

These proceedings provide the presentations of the invited speakers, brief summaries of the panel discussions that were prepared by designated rapporteurs, and a summary of the workshop. The NEA will prepare, in addition to these proceedings, a short document summarising the policy results from this first NEA/ICRP forum. It will be posted on the NEA website at www.nea.fr.

TABLE OF CONTENTS

WELCOME AND FORUM OPENING

OPENING ADDRESS

Kazuo Shimomura
Deputy Director Safety and Regulation, OECD Nuclear Energy Agency

Ladies and Gentlemen, Friends and Colleagues,

On behalf of the OECD Nuclear Energy Agency, I would like to welcome you to this first NEA Forum on Radiological Protection of the Environment, organised in collaboration with the International Commission on Radiological Protection – ICRP. The NEA is very appreciative of the efforts made by *Agenzia Nazionale per la Protezione dell'Ambiente* (ANPA) to host this meeting, and also grateful to the Vice-Major of Taormina for inviting us to his lovely town. Collaboration with the ICRP in the development of this Forum, especially the active support of its chair Professor Roger Clarke, has been essential and is welcomed by the NEA. I would also like to thank all of you for the interest you have shown in this important subject and the efforts you have made to attend the meeting. The programme promises an interesting meeting, and your support will, I am sure, lead to useful results.

The Nuclear Energy Agency was established in 1958 as a semi-autonomous body of the Organisation for Economic Co-operation and Development, and currently includes 27 Member countries from Europe, North America and the Pacific area. The NEA is organised through a Steering Committee for Nuclear Energy under the OECD Council and performs its technical programme through seven standing technical committees and a Data Bank. The Committee on Radiation Protection and Public Health (CRPPH) organises information exchange amongst senior policy makers, regulators, and senior representatives of research and development institutions from 27 NEA Member countries, in order to harmonise views on important radiation protection issues. The cross-party representation of industry, safety authorities, and governmental policy bodies make the CRPPH an uniquely placed international forum.

The most significant challenge currently facing the radiation protection community is how to better integrate radiation protection within modern concepts of and approaches to risk governance. In response to this issue, the internationally accepted principles of radiation protection, upon which virtually all national legislation is based, are in the process of being reviewed and updated. The CRPPH goal is to ensure that consensus on directions for improvement is reached among radiation protection experts from national regulatory authorities, and that this consensus is taken into account during the development of new approaches and international recommendations. This will be the Committee's main focus for the coming years.

With Roger Clarke's proposal for a future system of radiological protection, the ICRP opened the discussion to the interested community and began the process of developing new recommendations. The NEA is very grateful for the opportunity to engage in this dialogue with the ICRP, and as a first contribution the CRPPH performed and published *A Critical Review of the System of Radiation Protection.* As a direct follow-up, the CRPPH focused on specific items identified in the *Critical Review*, and suggested specific improvements for a modified system of radiological protection which will soon be published as *The Way Forward.*

Regarding the radiological protection of the environment, the *Critical Review* concluded that the rationale for making or not making recommendations should be more thoroughly and openly discussed by the ICRP and other stakeholders. The NEA therefore decided to organise, in collaboration with the ICRP, a series of three fora to promote and establish a process to assist the development of national policies and international consensus for radiological protection of the environment

This first Forum, over the following three days, shall foster discussion and consensus building on open questions regarding radiological protection of the environment, involving a broad range of interested parties. The second Forum is planned "half-way" through the process, following reflections and draft consideration by the ICRP. A third and final NEA Forum is planned following the publication of the ICRP recommendation, and will focus on aspects regarding the implementation of this recommendation in NEA Member countries.

Which are the open questions we have to address during this Forum? Our Programme is divided into four sessions which will focus on the following issues:

- What problem are we trying to solve? Is there an international rationale behind the wish to protect the environment from radiation?

- Do we have enough scientific information to develop and define a broadly accepted policy?

- What are the socio-political dynamics, beyond science, that will influence policy on radiological protection of the environment?

- What are the characteristics of the process for developing a system of radiological protection of the environment?

We believe that the presentations, together with the panel discussions after each session, will assist in answering these questions.

We are very grateful that the *Agenzia Nazionale per la Protezione dell'Ambiente* (ANPA) kindly offered to host the first NEA Forum in this beautiful location. We welcome the participation from NEA Member countries, intergovernmental organisations, non-governmental organisations, politics, science, sociology and industry. It is planned to publish proceedings of this first NEA Forum including the presentations made and the outcome of the panel discussions. In addition, a small booklet is planned to summarise the conclusions of this Forum.

Let me finally express my hope, that this initiative will assist both the NEA Member countries to develop common views among governmental policy advisors, regulators and implementers, and the ICRP in broadening the information basis and discussion input needed for its process of the development of new recommendations.

Again, I would like to thank you, in advance, for what I am sure will be very fruitful discussions. I look forward to participating in these discussions, and to listening and contributing during this Forum.

WHAT DOES ICRP EXPECT FROM THESE FORA?

Roger Clarke
ICRP Chairman, United Kingdom

The current ICRP policy

It was in the 1977 ICRP Recommendations (Publication 26) that the Commission first recognised the need to consider species other than humans. The principal objective was said to be the achievement and maintenance of appropriately safe conditions for activities involving human exposure. Paragraph 14 states:

> "The level of safety required for the protection of all human individuals is thought likely to be adequate to protect other species, although not necessarily individual members of those species. The Commission therefore believes that if man is adequately protected then other living things are likely to be sufficiently protected."

In the 1990 Recommendations (Publication 60) these views were restated but with the same intentions and philosophy (Paragraph 16):

> "The Commission believes that the standard of environmental control needed to protect man to the degree currently thought desirable will ensure that other species are not put at risk."

> "At the present time, the Commission concerns itself with mankind's environment only with regard to the transfer of radionuclides through the environment, since this directly affects the radiological protection of man."

As the Commission begins to think about radiological protection at the start of the 21st century, these statements need to be reconsidered.

Underlying assumptions

The Commission view to date has clearly been that the environment is protected through the protection of mankind. Furthermore it has said that the appropriate level of protection is to avoid endangering the existence of species, or creating ecological imbalance which acknowledges the fact that individual members of a species may be harmed. Then it is clear that reproductive capacity is the relevant endpoint.

ICRP has not explicitly stated that the environment should be protected. However, the policy that the Commission has recommended does provide for some protection of the environment.

The policy in practice

Protection of the environment has, indirectly, been enhanced through application of the principle of optimisation of protection. The requirement that doses to people should be as low as reasonably achievable (ALARA) means that in most cases doses to other species have been reduced.

However there are clearly circumstances where the ICRP statement is not sufficient to protect the environment. Some immediate examples would be:

- Environments where the human is absent.

- A situation where people have been removed for their own safety.

- Where the distribution of radionuclides in the environment is such that the exposure to humans would be minimal, but other organisms could be considerably exposed.

It is time for ICRP to address these situations.

International guidance

On the international scene there has been a shift in the approach of society, from a purely anthropocentric view to include biocentric aspects. This is reflected in an emphasis on sustainability, conservation and biological diversity. The international activities that are most relevant are:

- The 1996 UNSCEAR report on "Effects of radiation on the environment".

- Environmental protection is addressed by the IAEA in their Safety Series and a document is currently being developed for environmental protection.

- Joint Convention on the Safety of Spent Nuclear Fuel Management and Radioactive Waste Management, which is serviced by the IAEA, includes protection of individuals, society and the environment.

- The Oslo-Paris Commission declared in the Cintra statement the ultimate aim of concentrations in the environment near background values for naturally occurring, and close to zero for artificial, radioactive substances.

Why an ICRP system for the environment?

At present there are no explicit sets of criteria, standards or a philosophy for radiological protection of the environment that has international authority or endorsement. There is, undeniably, a need to demonstrate that the environment is adequately protected. In addition, several countries are already implementing environmental radiation standards and international agreement would facilitate this process more widely.

The protection of the environment is a goal in itself, but in addition it may be thought necessary to protect the environment in order to safeguard the future well being of mankind.

ICRP Task Group on protection of the environment

The Main Commission has decided to establish its own Task Group on the subject of protection of the environment. It is charged with developing a protection policy and suggesting a framework for radiological protection of the environment. It is chaired by the Vice-Chairman of the Commission, Lars-Erik Holm from Sweden and has as members:

- Rudolf Alexakhin, Russian Federation.
- Jan Pentreath, United Kingdom.
- Kirstin Shrader-Frechette, United States.
- Per Strand, Norway.
- Patsy-Ann Thompson, Canada.

It is envisaged that the Task Group will have finished its work in time for a policy to be included in the recommendations for the start of the 21st century being prepared by the main Commission. Dr Holm will describe the progress being made by the Task Group at this forum.

What might these fora help to achieve?

ICRP is collaborating with the NEA is holding these three proposed fora. The aspirations of the Main Commission as a result of this initiative might be summarised as:

- to establish a clear set of objectives and principles for radiological protection of the environment;
- to summarise the basic knowledge of radiation effects in species other than the human;
- to agree a set of quantities and units to apply the policy;
- to develop a means of demonstrating compliance with the agreed criteria;

and, if appropriate,

- to define a reference set of dose models for a number of reference fauna and flora?

I hope to be able to conclude at the end of this meeting that we are making progress on these issues.

SESSION 1

The Rationale Behind a New Approach to Protect the Environment from Radiation

Chair: Rick Jones, Chairman of CRPPH,
Department of Energy, United States

A. Taking Stock of International, Regional and National Developments

THE DEVELOPMENT OF THE IAEA POLICY ON THE RADIOLOGICAL PROTECTION OF THE ENVIRONMENT

Gordon Linsley

Waste Safety Section, International Atomic Energy Agency, Vienna, Austria

Abstract

Since its creation in 1957, and in accordance with its statute, the IAEA has established standards of safety for protection of health in the fields of nuclear installations safety, radiation protection, the transport of radioactive materials and radioactive waste management, including the control of radioactive releases to the environment. In this context, the IAEA has a long history of involvement in matters related not only to the protection of humans but also to the protection of other species from the effects of radioactivity in the environment.

Concern about the environment has arisen for different reasons over the years, starting with questions about the potential effects on non-human species of fall-out from nuclear weapons testing and of radioactive discharges to atmosphere and the oceans. Later, the concern was focussed on the possible harm to non-human species caused by the dumping of solid waste at sea. The IAEA has responded to requests from other UN bodies and from international conventions to evaluate these potential hazards and to establish protection criteria.

Social and political attitudes have gradually changed towards the environment mainly due to a growing realisation that the environment is vulnerable to the effects of human activities. This change has been reflected in the outcomes of major UN conferences on the environment in 1972 and 1992 and, accordingly, the emphasis of international and national policies towards the environment has increasingly shifted towards protective measures and strategies that include other species. Thus, the protection of the environment from the effects of ionising radiation has taken on a new importance.

The IAEA, together with other relevant international organisations, is working to develop an agreed environmental protection strategy to counter the possible effects of ionising radiation, building on the work done over the last 30 years but taking due account of the new attitudes to the subject. The IAEA's ultimate goal is to develop safety standards on the protection of the environment from the effects of ionising radiation that have the full consensus of its Member States.

1.   Introduction

The Statute of the International Atomic Energy Agency (IAEA) obliges it to establish or adopt standards of safety for protection of health and minimization of danger to life and property and to provide for the application of these standards. The IAEA has been fulfilling this obligation since shortly after its statute was approved in 1956. Safety standards have been issued in the fields of nuclear safety, transport of radioactive materials, radiation protection and radioactive waste management. The standards are issued with the approval of the Member States of the IAEA, which currently number 132. A comprehensive system of committees of national safety regulators and experts has been established within the IAEA to provide for the technical review and approval of the standards. The process also involves formal review of draft documents by Member States and the final step is approval by the IAEA Board of Governors, for top level documents.

The role of the International Commission on Radiological Protection (ICRP) in relation to the standards was established in 1960 when, at a Board of Governors meeting, it was agreed that "The Agency's basic safety standards will be based, to the extent possible, on the recommendations of the International Commission on Radiological Protection (ICRP)". Successive editions of the basic safety standards on radiation protection have had their basis in the relevant recommendations of the ICRP. The most recent is the International Basic Safety Standards for Protection against Ionizing Radiation and for the Safety of Radiation Sources (the BSS)(IAEA, Safety Series No.115 (1995)) which is co-sponsored by FAO, ILO, OECD/NEA, PAHO, and WHO.

The IAEA has a long history of providing advice and recommendations related to radioactive materials in the environment. Within five years of the approval of its statute, a Safety Series report was issued on Radioactive Waste Disposal into the Sea (Safety Series No.5 (1961)). Others soon followed dealing with the control of waste disposal into fresh water and into the ground. While there is no mention of "environment" in the IAEA Statute it is obvious from the early Safety Series reports that it was implicitly assumed that practices involving the dispersion or deposition of radioactive materials in the environment would be subject to hazard assessments. In fact, the word "environment" does not appear in IAEA documents until much later, reflecting the gradual change which occurred in the way in which society viewed the place in which it lived. In the 1960s concern in relation to radioactive materials and other pollutants in the environment was almost entirely directed at their effects on humans. Consideration of other species was mainly limited to the possible harm that could be caused to them as potential human food resources.

2.   IAEA commitments to protection of the environment

The current BSS follows the ICRP Publication 60 position in relation to protection of the environment and states: "The scope of the Standards is limited to protection of human beings only; it is considered that standards of protection that are adequate for this purpose will also ensure that no other species is threatened as a population, even if individuals of the species may be harmed."

However, other high level safety standards of the IAEA reflect the changes which have occurred in the past decade in attitudes towards the environment. The concerns expressed at the United Nations Conference on Environment and Development in Rio in 1992 for sustainable development and protection of the environment are reflected in the Safety Fundamentals document "The Principles of Radioactive Waste Management" issued as Safety Series no.111-F in 1995. The first five of nine principles are concerned with:

- Protection of human health.
- Protection of the environment.
- Protection beyond national boundaries.
- Protection of future generations.
- Burdens on future generations.

Here, for the first time, the requirement for protection of the environment is separated from the requirement for protection of human health. Principle 2 requires that: "Radioactive waste shall be managed in such a way as to provide an acceptable level of protection of the environment". The other principles reflect the concern for sustainability and the right of other states to be consulted.

The Safety Fundamentals document on was used as the technical basis for the development of the Joint Convention on the Safety of Spent Fuel Management and on the Safety of Radioactive Waste Management which was adopted in 1997 and came into force in June 2001 (IAEA INFCIRC/546). Articles 4 and 11 of this convention state that: "Each Contracting Party shall take appropriate steps to ensure that at all stages of spent fuel management (radioactive waste management), individuals, society and the environment are adequately protected against radiological hazards".

The need to elaborate the meaning of Principle 2 of the Safety Fundamentals and Articles 4 and 11 of the Joint Convention has provided a stimulus for the current IAEA programme on developing guidance on protection of the environment from the effects of ionising radiation.

3. History of IAEA involvement in evaluating the environmental effects of ionising radiation

Some important milestones in the movement towards international policy development on environmental protection against ionising radiation are shown in Table 1.

3.1 Early days

In 1958 the UN Conference on the Law of the Sea recommended that the IAEA should be responsible for assisting States in controlling discharges, conducting studies and promulgating standards to prevent pollution due to radioactive materials. At this time the concern was over the possible hazards due to nuclear weapons fall-out, radioactive discharges from land and from nuclear ships and from waste disposal into the sea. Accordingly, the IAEA established expert panels to develop appropriate advice and several Safety Series reports were published in the 1960s. However, concern was limited to ensuring that humans were adequately protected.

There was a gradual change in attitudes towards the environment brought about by visible evidence of harm in various parts of the world caused by human activities, e.g., the effects of "acid rain". This change of attitude was clearly indicated in the Declaration of the UN Conference on the Human Environment (Stockholm, 1972) which, inter alia, called upon Governments to exert common efforts for the preservation and improvement of the human environment, for the benefit of all the people and for their posterity.

3.2 First IAEA assessment of effects on other species

In 1970, a panel of experts was convened by the IAEA to assess the principles for limiting the introduction of radioactive waste into the sea. This panel, in its conclusions, recommended pursuing some general areas of research, one of which was "the study of the effects of ionising radiation on organisms and their sensitive life stages with special regard to effects at the genetic, population and ecosystem level". Subsequently several expert meetings were held on the subject resulting in the publication, in 1976, of IAEA Technical Reports Series No.172 with the title "Effects of Ionizing Radiation on Aquatic Organisms and Ecosystems". The report was in three parts. In the first part, typical concentrations of radionuclides in aquatic environments due to nuclear weapons fallout and as a result of some typical discharge practices into rivers and to coastal sea areas were reviewed and the resulting radiation doses to aquatic organisms assessed. In the second part, the available information on the effects of ionising radiation on aquatic organisms was summarised. In the final part, the possible effects of the estimated radiation doses from typical existing environmental concentrations on fish populations were evaluated. It was concluded that "it would appear that there are no deleterious effects on populations at the doses and dose rates estimated in (the first part of the study)". However it was recognised that there were deficiencies in the available information on the concentrations of radionuclides in the aquatic environment, especially of naturally occurring radionuclides, on suitable dosimetric models and on the effects of low radiation dose rates on marine species. Consequently, recommendations were made for research to be conducted in these areas. Methodologies for assessing the impact of radioactive materials in aquatic environments were subsequently reviewed at an IAEA Advisory Group Meeting held in 1977 (IAEA Technical Reports Series No. 190 (1979)).

3.3   *Impact of sea dumping on other species*

Towards the end of the 1970s, the practice of dumping solid radioactive waste at sea came under increasing scrutiny. In 1975, an international legal framework was established to control and monitor the practice of sea dumping of all types of waste. It was the Convention on the Prevention of Marine Pollution by Dumping of Wastes and Other Matter, now known as the London Convention, 1972, but formerly as the London Dumping Convention. The IAEA was required, under this convention, "to define high level radioactive waste or other high level radioactive matter unsuitable for dumping at sea....and to recommend a basis for issuing special permits for dumping (other types of) radioactive materials...". The IAEA first issued its Definition in 1976, revised it in 1978 and again in 1985. In this last version, known as the 1986 Edition,[1] the radiological basis for the Definition was that the practice of sea dumping should not lead to an annual radiation dose to the critical group of human individuals in excess of 1mSv . Calculations were performed which took account of the release of radionuclides from dumped packages (assumed conservatively to be released instantaneously on reaching the sea bed), subsequent dispersion and dilution in the ocean, concentration in human foodstuffs or deposition on a coastline and, finally, exposure of humans through their consumption of marine derived foodstuffs or exposure to a coastline deposit (or other related pathways). Although the Definition was based on human radiological protection considerations, there was, nevertheless, concern over the possible effects of the sea dumping of radioactive waste on marine organisms at the population level and it was recommended that further work on this matter be undertaken.[2]

Starting in 1985, the IAEA began an exploration of the possible effects of the sea dumping of radioactive waste packages on marine species. The possible radiation dose rates to typical marine species as a result of the assumed instantaneous release of radionuclides from waste dumped at the rates allowed by the Definition, were estimated They were compared with the available information on the effects of radiation on marine species. The results of the study were published as IAEA Technical Reports Series No 288 in 1988, with the title "Assessing the Impact of Deep Sea Disposal of Low

---

1. International Atomic Energy Agency, Definition and Recommendations for the Convention on the Prevention of Marine Pollution by Dumping of Wastes and Other Matter, 1972, 1986 Edition, Safety Series No. 78, IAEA, Vienna (1986).

2. Annex to the revised Derinition and Recommendations submitted to the IAEA Board of Governors in 1985 (GOV/2218).

Level Radioactive Waste on Living Marine Resources". The report concludes that "certain radionuclides, such as Zn-65 and other neutron activation gamma emitting nuclides (americium-241, radium-228 and thorium-229), if dumped according to the assumptions used in the calculations establishing the Definition could be expected to result in dose rates, sustained over a sufficiently large area, that have some degree of environmental impact". It was recommended that future revisions of the Definition should take into account potential environmental effects.

In 1983, a voluntary moratorium on the sea dumping of radioactive waste was agreed by Contracting Parties to the London Convention and, in 1994, it was replaced by a formal prohibition of the practice. The 1986 Edition was the last version of the Definition issued by the IAEA and so the recommendations of Technical Reports Series No. 288 with regard to consideration of environmental effects in establishing the Definition were never implemented.

3.4   *Impact on species in the terrestrial and freshwater environments*

During the 1980's, the prevailing international position with regard to the protection of species other than humans was that established by the ICRP in its Publication 26 (1977): "…the level of safety required for the protection of all human individuals is thought likely to be adequate to protect other species, although not necessarily individual members of those species". From time to time the ICRP approach was questioned, for example, during international meetings organised by the IAEA concerned with setting standards for controlling releases of radionuclides to the environment. It was reported at one of these meetings that standards had been established in the Soviet Union for the protection of fish in freshwater and, while it was difficult at that time to establish the basis for such standards, the report did serve to feed the belief among experts that the subject needed attention.

In 1986, an IAEA project was instigated to examine the validity of the ICRP assumption for the case of radioactive releases to the terrestrial and freshwater environments. The basic approach adopted was as follows: 1) the available information on the effects of ionising radiation on natural organisms was reviewed, 2) the radiation doses and/or dose rates above which there are deleterious effects on populations of different types of plants and animals were determined, 3) the radiation doses and/or dose rates to plants and animals which result when releases of radionuclides are controlled on the basis of the standards for the protection of humans were estimated (by modelling techniques) and 4) the radiation doses and dose rates in 2) and 3) were compared to establish whether or not plant and animal populations are afforded adequate protection under radiation protection standards for humans.

The results of the study were published as IAEA Technical Reports Series No.332 in 1992 entitled "Effects of Ionising Radiation on Plants and Animals at Levels Implied by Current Radiation Protection Standards". It was concluded that "There is no convincing evidence … that chronic radiation dose rates below 1mGy/d will harm animal or plant populations. It is highly probable that limitation of the exposure of the most exposed humans living on and receiving full sustenance from the local area, to 1mSv/a will lead to dose rates to plants and animals in the same area of less than 1mGy/d. Therefore, specific radiation protection standards for non-human biota are not needed". Some possible exceptions were noted: where the exposed human population group is separated geographically from a potentially exposed population of organisms, rare and endangered populations with very low fecundity and populations already under stress from a variety of natural or man-made pressures. The report recommended that each of these situations should be assessed on a site specific basis.

3.5   *Changing environmental policies*

A new focus and importance was given to environmental protection by the United Nations Conference on Environment and Development (UNCED) Earth Summit in Rio de Janeiro in 1992. The Rio Declaration on Environment and Development emphasises the issue of sustainable development, implying that development should only take place with proper consideration of the use and maintenance of natural resources. It was agreed that "environmental protection shall constitute an integral part of the development process and cannot be considered in isolation from it". After this, explicit requirements that the environment should be protected began to appear in national legislation and in international standards and legal instruments. As mentioned in section 2, in the field of radioactive waste management the IAEA Safety Fundamentals "The Principles of Radioactive Waste Management" (1995) and the Joint Convention on the Safety of Spent Fuel Management and on the Safety of Radioactive Waste Management (1997) both contain explicit requirements that the environment is protected.

It became increasingly evident that consideration of the protection of species other than humans was needed, even though the earlier studies in the marine, freshwater and terrestrial environments had indicated that there was no evidence of harm.

Starting in 1997, the IAEA began to look again at the issue of environmental protection and in 1999, after several meetings of international experts, it published an informal report for discussion. The report, IAEA-TECDOC 1091, "Protection of the Environment from Effects of Ionising Radiation", discussed the need for new policies and listed the following reasons to examine the subject further:

- ICRP statements might not apply to all time and space or under all conditions;

- the lack of specific environmental protection criteria or standards may undermine public confidence;

- there is an inconsistency in the approach adopted when compared with other environmental pollutants;

- there is no internationally endorsed method for providing assurance that present measures for protection of the environment are adequate.

4.   A programme to develop standards on environmental protection

Subsequently, the IAEA has established a programme to develop international standards for protecting the environment from the effects of ionising radiation.

The IAEA's programme has two parts; the first is aimed at promoting information exchange, and the second is aimed at developing safety standards.

The aim of the programme on information exchange is to provide a forum for reporting on the research work which is going on in several countries, including the programmes of research sponsored by the European Union. In 2000 and 2001, Specialists Meetings (or Workshops) were held in Vienna. They included sessions of individual presentations followed by meetings of working groups to discuss specific issues. In 2002, instead of the Specialists Meeting, an international conference is being held in Darwin, Australia, organised by the various federal governmental organisations concerned with radiation protection in cooperation with the IAEA. In 2003, the IAEA will organise an international conference in Stockholm, hosted by the Swedish Radiation Protection Authority. The conference will promote the discussion of issues related to the development of a coherent international policy on environmental radiation protection.

In parallel, the IAEA has organised a series of small meetings of experts with the aim of working towards a new environmental protection policy or framework. The ideas generated by these groups have been exchanged with the participants of the Specialists Meetings as well as with the ICRP task group which is addressing the subject. Earlier this year an IAEA report based on the work of the expert groups, addressing ethical aspects of the subject, was published on "Ethical considerations in protecting the environment from the effects of ionising radiation, "(IAEA-TECDOC-1270). In the longer term, the expert groups are working towards developing a safety standard while recognising that coordination with other international groups will be necessary. The process is under way but it is likely to take several more years before a consensus standard can be agreed upon.

Table 1. **Milestones in the establishment of an environmental protection policy**

1958	Geneva, UN Conference on Law of the Sea – recommends IAEA responsibility for promulgating standards to prevent pollution due to radioactive materials
1950s and 1960s	Concern for human well-being in relation to fallout, discharges from land and nuclear ships and waste disposal at sea
1972	Stockholm, UN Conference on Human Environment – reflects increased concern for the environment
1976	First IAEA explicit consideration of non-human species (IAEA-TRS-172)
1980s	London Convention, 1972 – impacts of sea dumping on non-human species
1987	Brundtland report, emphasises sustainable development including environmental protection
1992	UNCED, Rio – general principles for environmental protection
1996	International Symposium on Ionising Radiation: Protection of the Natural Environment (Stockholm)
2003	IAEA Conference on Protection of the Environment from the Effects of Ionising Radiation (Stockholm)

PROTECTION OF THE ENVIRONMENT – VIEWS FROM THE NORDIC MEETING ON ENVIRONMENTAL RADIOLOGICAL PROTECTION

Sigurdur M. Magnusson
Icelandic Radiation Protection Institute, Iceland

Ladies and gentlemen, friends and colleagues.

It is a great pleasure and privilege for me to present views from a Nordic meeting on environmental radiation protection at this NEA/ICRP Forum on the Radiological Protection of the Environment.

I wish to take the opportunity to extend my sincere thanks to Rick Jones, the chairman of CRPPH at NEA, and Roger Clarke, the chairman of ICRP, for taking the initiative to this timely Forum. To have the Forum in Sicily in these impressive surroundings so close to the mountain Etna helps to put the conference in a proper perspective.

The Nordic meeting was actually a Consensus Conference on Protection of the Environment which was part of the Seminar *Radiation Protection in the 21st Century: Ethical, Philosophical and Environmental Issues* held at the Norwegian Academy of Science and Letters, (Oslo, October 22-25 2001).

The seminar was chaired in a very competent way by Per Strand and Deborah Oughton, who is with us here today, and arranged by the Norwegian Radiation Protection Authority and the Agricultural University of Norway, on behalf of Nordic Nuclear Safety Research (NKS), in co-operation with the International Union of Radioecology (IUR).

Now a few words on Nordic Nuclear Safety Research (NKS) since I assume that many of you are not familiar with this organisation.

NKS is a scientific co-operation program mainly financed by the national Nordic authorities in nuclear safety, radiation protection and emergency preparedness, with additional support from the nuclear power industry, research establishments and the academic world in the Nordic countries. The purpose of NKS is to carry out joint, cost-effective Nordic projects, thus producing research results, exercises, reports, scientific papers, manuals, recommendations and other material. This material serves as an input to decision-makers and other concerned staff members from the organisations involved in the NKS activities. In the present program, a number of projects are carried out in the fields of reactor safety, radioactive waste, emergency preparedness, radioecology and nuclear threats in Nordic surroundings.

The aim of the consensus conference was to provide a forum for discussion of current issues in radiation protection and the environment, to provide input into international developments related to the protection of the environment, and to encourage wider participation in the debate. There were 45 participants, about 50% from the Nordic countries, representing various disciplines including Environmental Science, Health Physics, Radioecology, Ethics and Philosophy. They represented a wide spectrum of perspectives bearing on the question of radiation protection of the environment. There were stimulating and thought provoking presentations in plenum followed by constructive and intensive group discussions. These were reported and continued in plenum. In this way the main areas of agreement concerning guiding principles and consensus statements were developed.

The Final Consensus Statement, copies of which are available, reflects the views of the individual participants giving their consent to the Statement and not, necessarily, those of NKS or the organisations employing them. Out of the 45 participants, 38 have given their written consent to the Statement, their names are included in the *Final Consensus Statement*. Out of the 38 consenting participants we have 8 present at this Forum.

The participants of the meeting took as a starting point that:

- The next decade is likely to bring significant improvement in radiation protection.

- A number of international bodies are currently considering the development of systems for protection of the environment from ionising radiation.

- The nuclear industry, authorities and regulators are faced with increasing challenges on the practical application of policy, notably the need to address more widely such values as transparency and stakeholder involvement.

Furthermore they agreed on the following Guiding Principles for environmental radiation protection:

- Humans are an integral part of the environment, and whilst it can be argued that it is ethically justified to regard human dignity and needs as privileged, it is also necessary to provide adequate protection of the environment.

- In addition to science, policy making for environmental protection must include social, philosophical, ethical (including the fair distribution of harms/benefits), political and economic considerations. The development of such policy should be conducted in an open, transparent and participatory manner.

- The same general principles for protection of the environment should apply to all contaminants.

And finally the participants agreed on the following Statements concerning environmental radiation protection:

- As part of the effort to revise and simplify the current system of radiological protection for humans, there is a need to specifically address radiological protection of the environment.

- There are several reasons to protect the environment including ethical values, sustainable development, conservation (species and habitat) and bio-diversity.

- Our present level of knowledge should allow the development of a system that can be used to logically and transparently assess protection of the environment using appropriate end points. The development of the system ought to identify knowledge gaps and uncertainties that can be used to direct research to improve the system.

- The best available technology including consideration of economic costs and environmental benefits should be applied to control any release of radionuclides into the environment in a balanced manner with respect to other insults to the environment.

- When a product or activity may cause serious harm to the human population or to the environment, and significant uncertainties exist about the probability of harm, precautionary measures to reduce the potential risk within reasonable cost constraints should be applied. In making such assessments and decisions, an improved mechanism for incorporating developing scientific knowledge needs to be established.

- To assess the impact on the environment there is a need to take into account inter alia radiation type, type of organism, and biological endpoints (impact-related). In order to improve the transparency of assessing environmental impacts, the authoritative bodies should consequently give consideration to the development of quantities and units for biota, with the intent to avoid unnecessary complexity.

This concludes my report on the Nordic meeting on Environmental Radiation Protection. Copies of the Final Consensus Statement are available for those who are interested. Thank you very much.

Participants giving their consent to the Final Consensus Statement[*]

Rudolf Alexakhin, Ingar Amundsen, Peder Anker, Steinar Backe, Ingrid Bay, Torkel Bennerstedt, Richard Bramhall, Francois Brechignac, Anne Brekken, Gordon C. Christensen, David Copplestone, Riitta Hanninen, Mogens Bagger Hansen, George Hunter, Per Hedemann Jensen, Rick Jones, Karsten Klint Jensen, Terje Kvilhaug, Carl-Magnus Larsson, Sigurdur M. Magnusson, Randall C. Morris, Kenneth Mossman, Deborah Oughton, Jan Pentreath, Lars Persson, Carol Robinson, Jørn Roed, Brit Salbu, Lindis Skipperud, Helge Smidt Olsen, Graham Smith, William Standring, Helene Stensrud, Per Strand, Ulf Tveten, Arnfinn Tønnessen, Jack Valentin, Dennis Woodhead.

---

[*] The consensus statement reflects the views of the individual participants themselves and not, necessarily, those of the organisations employing them.

RADIOECOLOGY AND ENVIRONMENTAL ISSUES IN JAPAN: PAST AND PRESENT

Junko Matsubara
Nuclear Safety Commissioner, Japan

A bomb experience in 1945 and the death of Japanese fishermen, due to the fallout from a Nuclear Explosion Test at Bikini Atoll in 1954, have triggered a bulk of scientists to participate in the field of radioecology since the mid 1950s. Outbreaks of Minamata disease and Itaiitai disease due to organic Hg and Cd pollution to the sea and rivers from chemical industries, respectively, further stimulated people's concern about the environment. Because these events are the first examples that the common people, not workers, were endangered by the outsider or industrial activities. These impacts pushed the government for strict controls of pollutants in the environment and resulted in wide-spread monitoring networks both for radioactive and chemical pollutants.

Only 10% of materials are recycled with steadily increasing annual environmental loads in Japan. Even in our ecologically rich sea it is found that aquatic organisms are getting less resilient due to intense manmade input to the sea, while no environmental hazard was detected surrounding nuclear power stations during over 30 years of operation. Radioactive wastes are kept under strict control by the regulator.

The lessons we have learned are:

1. Regulator's role is important.

2. Environmental strategy should be holistic and monitoring should be comprehensive. By the analysis of monitoring data including sensitive indicators we can diagnose the resilience of the environment.

3. Proper estimation of the environmental loads, e.g. material balance at the local as well as the global level at present and in the future should be implemented.

4. Scenario-based implementation but flexibility for re-evaluation and/or reorientation is necessary.

Background

Japan consists of four long islands spreading across a latitude of 28-46 degrees in the north-temperate zone. People like nature and appreciate the varied climate so much that one can see the influence of the seasonal change even in our daily culture. People respect the nature as if it means the presence of God. People have taken for granted the coexistence with nature since olden times.

Past experiences and application of radioecological methods

Disasters in Hiroshima and Nagasaki with a nuclear bomb (causing approximately 75 000 deaths, 120 000 have been followed up in the Life Span Study since 1950) were really the most bitter experience for the Japanese as own man-made disasters during World War II. An event of radiation exposure to 23 Japanese fishermen (one of whom died), due to the fallout from Nuclear Explosion Testing at Bikini Atoll in 1954, triggered the activation of radioecological approach among radiation experts in Japan.

Ironically, the outbreaks of Minamata disease (organic mercury intoxication) caused nearly 200 deaths and Itaiitai disease (cadmium chronic intoxication of calcium deficient people) caused approximately 170 deaths among inhabitants during the 1950's caused by heavy-metal pollution to the sea and rivers from chemical industries should also be bench-marked. Because these events are the first example that not only workers but common people were endangered by industrial activities, they were symbolic events of environmental pollution to the public in Japan, even probably in the history of the world.

From 1945 to 1962 almost 500 megatons (200 were fissile) of nuclear explosive substances were introduced into the global atmosphere and spread on the ground by repeated nuclear explosion tests. Radiation monitoring networks in Japan were established as a special research project of the Ministry of Education. Figure 1 shows how precisely we could follow the local accumulation of the fallout (^{90}Sr) chronologically. Figure 2, reported by US scientists, shows the level of ^{90}Sr in cow's milk increases nearly proportional to the level of the ground deposit and the ^{90}Sr level in man reflects his metabolic activity at different ages.

Using radioisotopes as tracers one can investigate the kinetics of the elements in the body. The concepts of the discrimination factor and the critical organ were applied in our studies as shown in Figure 3, the quantitative food web of cadmium in man. Figure 4 demonstrates the relationship between the daily body intake of cadmium and the level of the deposit accumulated in the kidneys calculated by use of the compartment model. These are utilised for decision making for standard settings.

To cope with the above problems the government implemented the Factory Effluents Control Law in 1958. In accordance with fast development of industrial activities since the income-doubling programme installed in 1960 environmental pollution accelerated. Although Basic Law for Environmental Pollution Control was promulgated in 1970, which provides for the basic principles and framework regarding environmental pollution control measures, various suits were raised by the groups of sufferers. In 1971 the Environment Agency was established to co-ordinate and facilitate relevant environmental protection. We can see drastic improvement of our aquatic environment as indicated by the fast decrease of the percentages of the cases which do not fulfil the environmental criteria of toxic chemicals since 1971 up until the 1990s (see Figure 5).

Nuclear power station, people and the environment

Japan is a mountainous country with a dense population. The majority of people live in coastal or plain areas. All of the nuclear power plants are constructed so as to take advantage of sea-water cooling. until now in the areas where the policy of the promotion of nuclear energy is agreed by the people and local governments, stable coexistence among stakeholders, e.g. NPP staff, local inhabitants and fishermen, is kept. For instance, during the summer thousands of people enjoy swimming at the seashore exactly opposite Mihama NPP situated across a bridge of less than 1 km to the site boundary. In 1991 due to the improper setting of the tube-holders a SG tube in the steam generator ruptured. ECCS functioned and the reactor was safely shut down with discharge of a small amount of the contaminated steam. This event gave a big impact on the people although none of the environmental hazard was detected. This lesson to prevent accident was open to the public until now. Usually radioactive release is controlled to less than 50μSv per year as a voluntary goal during the normal operation by the atomic industry. The hot-water discharge to the sea is controlled properly and there have been no claims from the fishermen for 30 years of reactor operation in our country.

Efforts towards sustainable development

Meanwhile movements for the protection of the global environment were provoked internationally and people began to share a consensus for the efforts to establish sustainable development. In 1993 The Basic Environment Law was implemented. The purpose of the Basic Environment Law is, in a comprehensive and systematic manner, to promote measures for environmental conservation. The aim of these measures are to enable us to help obtain a healthy lifestyle for citizens and the welfare of humankind both in the present and in the future.

The illustration on Figure 6 is to describe the global circulation of mercury in our biosphere. One can discuss the problems of environmental safety and our resources for the future generation. It is already popular to discuss carbon-dioxide and/or energy circulation in the Biosphere regarding global warming. It is important for us to not only consider the present situation but also the future situation of the earth and people by means of a quantitative assessment. The global circulation of the substances was proved by the data of iodine 131. The released ^{131}I from the Chernobyl NPP was detected between 3-20 May 1986 at monitoring stations in various district of Japan, where several thousand kilometres away from Chernobyl (Cf. Figure 7). Thus radioecological methods provided people with a comprehensive and dynamic way of thinking about environmental problems.

Current environmental problems in Japan

The flow of materials into Japan as a whole, including loads to the environment, is illustrated on Figure 8. During 1999, Japan utilised a total of 2 billion tons of material consumption as inputs for its socio-economic activities. These materials, acquired both within Japan and overseas, included 1.75 billion tons of resources extracted from the natural environment. Of these input resources, approximately 50% was directly consumed and then disposed of. Of all the materials introduced, 0.2 billion tons(only 10%) were recycled for re-use as resources. Looking at Japan's material balance in this way shows that there is essentially a one-way flow from resource extraction to consumption and disposal. This situation is still very far from the ideal of a society based on environmentally sound cycling of materials. Each year about 250 million tons of industrial waste and 50 million tons of domestic waste are produced.

Presently we keep 132 000 drums of low-level waste from NPP Japan and 464 canisters of high-level waste at JNF Company, LTD in Rokkasho-mura. Apart from used fuels which are kept at the power station are supposed to be reprocessed into high-level waste in future for the reposition in a deep geologic repository after extraction of plutonium and vitrification. These radioactive wastes are strictly administered under the control and regulation by the government.

Environmental issues in Ariake

In early 2001 a sudden drop of the crop of cultured seaweed (edible red algae) in Isahaya bay in Ariake, Kyushu, triggered a big debate between the fishermen, environmental protectionists versus the local government and the constructor of the floodgate in order to reclaim land. The Expert's Committee analysed the various monitoring data on the biota, ecosystems including benthos, physico-chemical and socio-economical factors, and says that the main cause of the decrease of the crop was the outbreaks of poisonous red-diatoms as a result of eutrophication which were brought by the introduction of excessive nutrients from the coastal rivers and that abnormal climate in the previous year strengthened the effect. The next year fishermen had normal crops. The committee proposes that further continuation of the investigation for various factors related to the whole ecosystem in bay under the present situation before opening the water gate. In this case the construction of a sluice was not the real cause of the decrease of the algae. However, it is obvious that the long lasting man-made loads into the sea make aquatic biota/ecosystem less resilient and less adaptive. We should find out the environmental hazard using sensitive organisms heuristically. This suggests that importance of the holistic approach in order to protect our natural environment.

The lessons we have learned and proposals

1. Our experiences tell us that the regulator's role is important.

2. Environmental strategy should be holistic because environmental factors are inter-related.

3. The environmental monitoring should be comprehensive regarding both the natural and manmade factors. The analysis of monitoring data including sensitive indicator-organisms allow us to diagnose the resilience of the environment.

4. Proper estimation of the environmental loads, e.g. material balance at the local as well as the global level at present and also for the future should be implemented.

5. With analysing the collected data scenario-based implementation including flexibility for reevaluation and/or reorientation is necessary under the presence of uncertainty.

Figures

1. ^{90}Sr monthly ground deposit in Japan during 1962-1965(mCi/km^2).

2. Chronological increase of ^{90}Sr in the cumulative ground deposit, dry milk and children.

3. Food chain of cadmium from environmental foodstuffs to man. (Figures in boxes represent a daily g-intake in man with Cd concentration (ppm) in the diet).

4. Relationship between the estimated harmful level of Cd in the critical organ in a man at age 50 and the level of daily intake of Cd calculated with CM model with varied biological halflives (τ).

5a. Annual change in the percentages of violation of aquatic quality standards.

5b. Annual changes in the percentages of achievement of BOD/COD standards.

6. Global circulation of mercury.

7.   Level of I [131] in the air detected in various monitoring stations in Japan after the Chernobyl accident, 3rd-24th May 1986.

8.   Flow of materials in Japan as a whole.

9.   A view of beach near Mihama nuclear power station.

Figure 1. ^{90}Sr monthly ground deposit in Japan during 1962-1965 (mCi/km^2)

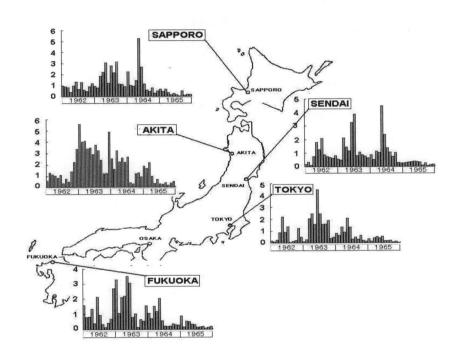

Figure 2. **Chronological increase of ⁹⁰Sr in the cumulative ground deposit,
dry milk and children**

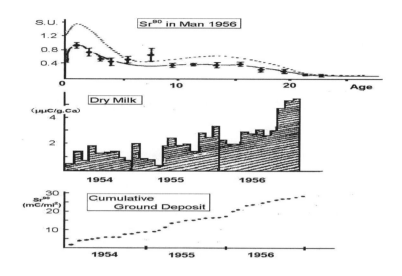

Figure 3. **Food chain of cadmium from environment foodstuffs to man**

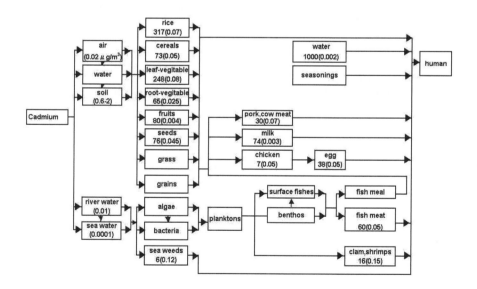

Figure 4. **Relationship between the estimated harmful level of Cd in the critical organ in man at age 50 and the level of daily intake of Cd calculated with CM model with varied biological halflives (τ)**

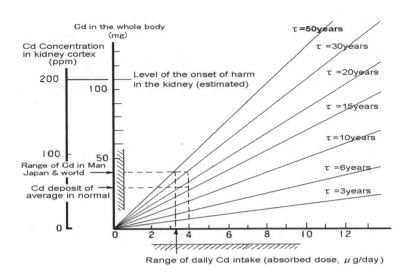

Figure 5a. **Annual change in the percentage of violation of aquatic standards**

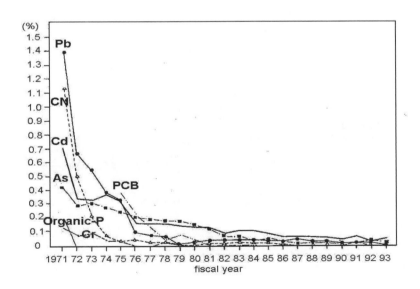

Figure 5b. **Annual change in the percentage of achievement of BOD/COD standards (Ministry of Environment)**

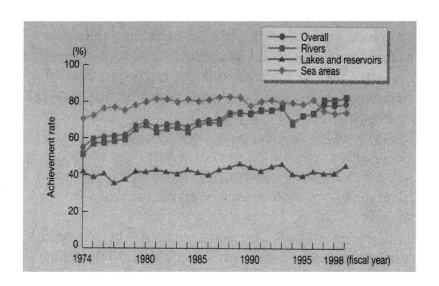

Figure 6. **Global circulation of mercury**

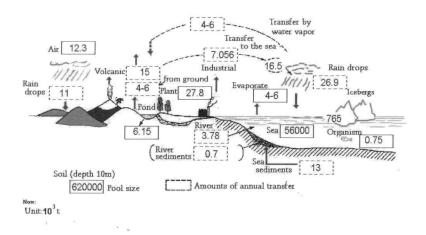

Figure 7. **Level of I[131] in the air detected in various monitoring stations in Japan after the Chernobyl accident during 3rd-24th May 1986 (Takizawa *et al.*)**

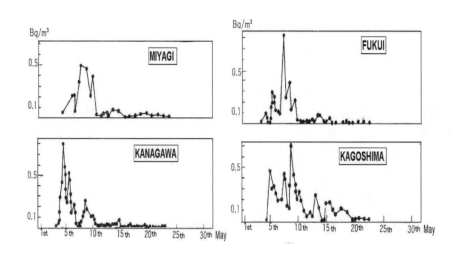

Figure 8. **Flow materials in Japan as a whole**

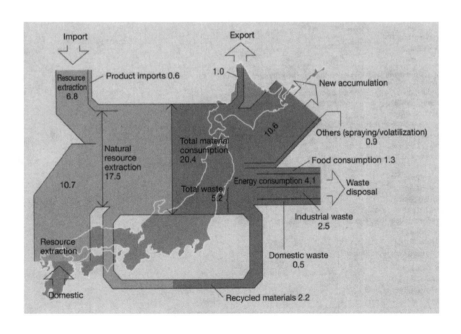

Figure 9. **A view of beach near Mihama nuclear power station**

B.   Specific Considerations

PROTECTION OF THE ENVIRONMENT FROM IONISING RADIATION: ETHICAL ISSUES

Deborah Oughton

Department of Chemistry and Biotechnology, Agricultural University of Norway,
International Union of Radioecologists

The paper identifies some of the main ethical issues concerning the protection of the environment from radiation and suggests ways in which ethics can aid in developing a system of protection. After a presentation of background on ethical theory and environmental ethics, three main issues related to practical environmental protection are discussed: First, the question of who or what has moral standing; second the appropriate level of protection; and third compatibility with other environmental stressors. In summary, the paper argues that there are strong ethical grounds for efforts to provide for the protection of the environment and that, all other things being equal, there is no reason to treat ionising radiation differently to other environmental stressors.

Keywords: Ethics, radiation protection, risk management, environmental philosophy, ecocentric, biocentric, anthropocentric.

1. Introduction

There is a growing awareness that radiation risk management needs to address the question of effects on the environment (Amiro, Avadhanula, Johansson, Larsson & Lüning 1996; Pentreath, 1998, 1999; Polikarpov, 1998). Yet developing and defending a practical and coherent system of protection for flora and fauna raises a number of ethical issues including the question of whether or not animals have moral status and why; how to define harm to the exposed population or individuals; how to balance the interests of humans against non-human species; and the fundamental question of why we should protect the environment in the first place. In common with many risk management policies, any answer to these problems will need to be based on both scientific knowledge and ethical values. Interestingly, many of the groups working on the issue of protection of the environment from radiation have identified a need to address the ethical and philosophical questions, including IAEA and ICRP. The aim of this paper is to identify some of the main ethical issues concerning the protection of the environment from radiation and suggest ways in which ethics can aid in developing a system of protection.

First, however, it is important to be aware that the field of moral philosophy is not without its own areas of contention and disagreement. There is no one theory of ethics to which decision makers can appeal to resolve conflicts. Furthermore, many real life controversies are grounded in fundamental ethical conflicts. With this in mind, the paper will give a short introduction to ethics, present different ethical theories and discuss some of the main areas of agreement and conflicts within environmental ethics and protection of the environment.

2.   Ethical evaluation

Ethics is the philosophical study of right and wrong conduct, and the rules and principles that ought to guide it. With respect to radiation risks, the conduct under scrutiny is practices and policies which cause people and the environment to be exposed to radiation, and interventions to reduce existing exposures. Since actions that either increase or avert radiation doses often have both positive and negative effects, and require trade-offs between those effects, ethical evaluation presents a particularly difficult challenge. It follows that the central question in radiation protection is one that is fundamental to moral philosophy: When can causing harm be ethically justified? The answer to that question depends partly on what one means by harm and partly on how one evaluates actions.

When evaluating actions, one of the most fundamental distinctions in ethics is that between ends and means. The end of an action is that for the sake of which it is performed (e.g., generating electricity, reducing doses to workers, disposal of radioactive waste); the means is the way in which the end is to be achieved (e.g., nuclear power, releasing radioactive waste to the environment, deep geological repositories). Different theories of ethics place different weights on ends and means; they attach different significance to the consequences of an action (i.e., on good or bad outcomes) against the way in which those consequences were attained, and have different rules for balancing favourable and adverse outcomes. In order to assess the possible harms of radiation exposure to flora and fauna, it is helpful to examine some of the major ethical theories and to look at the types of rules they say should guide decisions. The following section summarises three approaches to normative ethical theory: utilitarianism, deontology and contractualism, including their various stances on environmental ethics. These are by no means the only approaches to morality, but they do represent the heavyweights – at least in modern Western philosophy – and are diverse enough to cover the range of issues. Most importantly, the three doctrines differ with respect to the principles and rules they use to differentiate right from wrong, and the ways in which they balance ends and means.

3.   Three theories of ethics

3.1   *Utilitarianism and consequentialism*

Consequentialism is used to describe all ethical theories which assert that the moral value of an action derives entirely from the value of its consequences (Scheffler, 1988). Its adherents base judgements about right and wrong solely on the outcome of actions rather than the nature of the actions themselves. Utilitarianism is perhaps the most famous form of consequentialist ethics, and is characterised by three distinctive features. First, the value of consequences is measured in utility or happiness; second, the distribution of utility over populations does not matter; and, third, the moral value of conduct is judged by the amount of utility, or happiness, an action produces (Mill, 1871; Sen & Williams, 1982). The founder of utilitarianism was the English philosopher Jeremy Bentham (1748-1832), who made famous the theory that the proper end of action is to achieve the "greatest happiness of the greatest number" (Bentham, 1789).

Modern consequentialists tend to define utility in terms of welfare, interests or preference satisfaction (e.g., Hare, 1952, 1982; Singer, 1993), and many include animals in the calculation. The Australian philosopher, Peter Singer, is one of the most influential proponents of animal liberation ethics, and suggests that sentience represents the fundamental criterion for moral standing (Singer, 1991). Welfare or well-being matters for any life-form with the capacity to feel pleasure and pain. In this he advances an idea first proposed by Bentham when considering who or what should count in a utilitarian evaluation: "The question is not, Can they reason? Nor, Can they talk? But, Can they

46

suffer?" (Bentham, 1789). Many consequentialists retain the disquieting trait of classical utilitarianism whereby actions that bring about harm to a minority can be permitted if the benefit to the majority is large enough. The sum (or average) utility over the population is the cardinal measure of what is right. Although the calculation allows a hierarchical weighting of different species, human interests are not inalienable and can be outweighed if the amount of suffering caused to animals is large enough.

We can divide the major objections towards utilitarian and consequentialist ethics into empirical and intrinsic criticisms. Empirical problems arise because of the practical limitations to calculating the utility of an action that might have numerous possible expected outcomes, or because of the difficulty in reducing a variety of human (and non-human) preferences and values to a single unit (Hardin, 1988). There can be disputes over who and what to include in the calculations – animals, humans, future generations, and the ways these preferences are weighted. Hence the empirical critic claims that: "utilitarianism can't work, the calculation is out of the realms of human capability" or, if wanting to reject a particular utilitarian directive, he might simply say that "the calculation is wrong". Other critics claim that there is something intrinsically wrong with the way utilitarianism defines right and wrong; they point out that people simply do not (and should not) judge the moral worth of actions just by consequences. Damage to the environment is morally wrong for reasons other than its repercussions for human satisfaction (Rolston, 1991). They berate utilitarians for summing pleasure and pain indiscriminately across all individuals, for giving no direct weight to considerations of fairness, and for being able to support directives that violate human or animal rights (Rawls, 1971; Williams, 1988; Scheffler, 1994; MacIntyre, 1983).

3.2   *Deontological ethics*

In contrast to utilitarianism, deontological ethics takes the view that the moral value of an action is independent of its actual consequences, its value depends primarily on the type of act that it is. Thus deontologists and utilitarians disagree on a fundamental ethical issue: the deontologist claims that the ends do not justify the means, the utilitarian that the ends do justify the means.

The leading deontological system is that of the German philosopher Immanuel Kant (1724-1804). Kant's moral theory arises from the belief that man is free, and that his moral conviction is brought about by inner reasoning rather than by external forces (Kant, 1781). It follows that the eventual state of affairs obtained by a person's action might bear little weight in assessing the goodness or otherwise of moral behaviour. In deontological ethics (deon = duty), the right action is that which is performed out of a desire to act in accordance with the correct moral rules. For Kant, the fundamental moral right is to be treated as an end in oneself. The deontologists' concern for the individual gives rise to a set of conditions necessary for societies that accord human beings their full dignity, namely, *natural* or *human rights*. Respect for human autonomy and dignity is seen as being of central importance for *informed consent*, a principle developed particularly within medical ethics (Beauchamp and Childress, 1989), but increasingly applied in other areas such as the involvement of the public in the decision making process for waste management (Oughton and Bay, 2002).

Some environmental ethicists suggest that the notion of rights and duties should be extended to the animal or biological kingdom (Regan, 1980). Supporters of animal rights argue that, like humans, some non-human animals have consciousness or self-awareness and a capability for reasoning. Although Kant's philosophy was clearly human centred, his morality did include restrictions on what harms one might cause to animals. The rationale being that people who mistreat animals are likely to develop a habit that inclines them to treat humans in the same fashion (Kant, 1785; Regan & Singer, 1976). Similarly, one might argue that not showing respect for nature would foster an inclination to lose respect for one's fellow humans. Critics have claimed that the debate around giving "rights" to non-human species or indeed to whole ecosystems, is a futile response to the increasing tendency of human society towards environmental destruction. They draw parallels with the way as human rights have emerged as a well-meaning, and yet, to date, depressingly ineffective way of counteracting the modern day atrocities of warfare or racism (Bradford, 1993). The critique harks back to Bentham's notorious claim that "natural rights is simple nonsense; natural and imprescriptable rights, rhetorical nonsense – nonsense upon stilts (Bentham, 1824)". Nonetheless, human rights are being perceived as important by an increasing proportion of the world's population, and the possible future extension of these rights to other species is not easily dismissed. With respect to radiation protection, deontological ethics have a particular problem in how to classify actions that bring about a *risk* of harm (Oughton, 2001). Although the theory prohibits actions in which an agent knowingly harms human (or non-human) individuals, because this is seen as treating people (or animals) as means and a violation of rights or duties, it is unlikely that one can prohibit all actions which carry a risk of injury. It is difficult to find any action that does not carry some finite probability of resulting in harm to somebody or something (Thomson, 1986). The question facing the deontologist is whether or not exposing flora and fauna to radiation is treating them as means to an end?

3.3   *Contractualism*

A contractarian approach to ethics asks what principles or rules would be agreed upon by contracting parties under idealised conditions: the right thing to do being that which would be agreed upon in a hypothetical social contract. Historically, the idea of representing civil society as if it were established by a social contract derives from Thomas Hobbes (1588-1679) (Hobbes, 1651) and Jean-Jacques Rousseau (1712-1778) (Rousseau, 1755, 1762). Today, the principal example of this approach is that proposed by the American philosopher John Rawls in his seminal book: *A Theory of Justice* (Rawls, 1971). Rawls suggests that the principles or rules for a just society are those that would be chosen by rational people under conditions that force impartiality – conditions that are dramatised as an "original position". In the original position, rational agents with basic needs and interests choose principles from behind a metaphorical "veil of ignorance". By obscuring the role which they, themselves, will be allocated in society, the veil of ignorance strips agents of particular allegiances and interests, and forces them to choose principles which consider the interests of all groups in society. He goes on to argue that the rational choice from such a position would include both a basic framework of liberties, and a special concern for the least-well off, namely "distributive justice". Distributive justice states that social benefits and burdens be allocated in such a way as to make the position of the least well-off group as good as it could be. However, there is a certain amount of disagreement between contractarians about whom one is actually entering into a social contract with. Is this contract only with those capable of reciprocal action (i.e., living humans and the next couple of generations) or does it also include hypothetical contractees such as distant generations and animals?

In contrast to utilitarian (net consequences) and deontological ethics (individual rights), contractualism focuses primarily on the ethical dimension of equity, specifically a fair distribution of harms and benefits. As for any broadly egalitarian philosophy the main problem is at what level equality to be preserved: equal treatment or equal outcome. Is it enough to give all persons a fundamental right to liberty; should everybody have the same access to social goods; or should these goods be distributed equally. With respect to radiation protection and environmental ethics, one needs to focus not only on distribution over space but also over time (i.e., future generations) and species. Paying due attention to the distribution and balancing of burdens and benefits is particularly important for the practical management of environmental risks. Environmental justice relates to issues of liability, compensation and distribution, and is embodied in a number of policy principles such as polluter pays, best available technology and the precautionary approach.

4. Valuing the environment: common ethical principles

Despite the apparent diversity of these three doctrines, it is important to realise that although ethical theories may disagree quite strongly over *why*, exactly, certain factors are relevant to ethics, and which principle should be superior in cases of conflict, there can still be room for consensus on some common features. For an evaluation of any action involving exposure of humans, animals or plants to radiation, each of the above theories would find it morally-relevant to ask: 1) who and what is being affected; 2) what is the relative size of the benefits and the harms arising from the exposure; 3) what is the distribution of the risks and the benefits; 4) who has been involved in the decision making process; and, 5) what alternative courses of action are available?

With respect to protection of the environment and non-human species, all theories can defend the principle that radiation protection should not be limited to humans. Since regulations already exist for the protection of the environment from other pollutants, all other things being equal, there is no ethically relevant reason why effects caused by radiation exposure should be treated differently. However, it should be clear that the different theories might disagree on which types of effects matter most, depending for example on whether harms are evaluated in terms of sentience, animal rights, consequences for existing humans or effects on future generations. The conflicts that might arise in practical policy depend not so much on *whether* damaging the environment is wrong as *why* it is wrong. We can divide the discussions into philosophical questions of ethics and value (i.e., why the environment matters in risk evaluation), and policy questions attributable to the distribution of risks and benefits and their management (i.e., how to protect the environment).

4.1 Anthropocentric and non-anthropocentric ethics

Environmental ethicists have been debating the matter of why one attaches value to the environment for a number of decades (Rolston, 1988; Sterba, 1994). Central philosophical issues include the question of moral standing and whether the environment has intrinsic or inherent value (i.e., value in itself) or extrinsic or instrumental value (i.e., value because of human interest). Although environmental ethics is a relatively young field within philosophy, a number of distinct views on this question have emerged. In contemporary environmental philosophy, the most fundamental source of divergence arises between the anthropocentric and the non-anthropocentric view. An anthropocentric ethic (literally human centred) alleges that only humans have moral status and that environmental degradation matters only in so far as it influences human interests (Norton, 1988; Bookchin, 1991). Proponents of a non-anthropocentric ethic reject this assumption, and attribute moral status either to other living organisms or to the ecosystem as a whole, contending that effects on the environment matter irrespective of their consequences for humans. Although a variety of different views can be found in the literature, the biocentric and ecocentric outlooks are arguably the two main contenders.

Proponents of biocentrism (literally "life-centred") assert that individual life-forms other than humans can have moral standing, and should be respected for what they are – not only because they affect the interests of humans. Different biocentric views exist as to which criterion forms the basis for moral standing, and what hierarchy (if any) exists between different species. But all views derive moral value from some biological characteristic of individual members of species, such as sentience or the ability to feel pleasure or pain (Singer, 1976), self-consciousness (Regan, 1980) or inherent worth or a "good of their own" of all living things (Taylor, 1986; Goodpaster, 1978). Because biocentrism focuses on individuals rather than the diversity of species, these various outlooks have also been described as an "individualistic" environmental ethic (Sagoff, 1984; Rolston, 1991). In practical policy-making, biocentric outlooks have had the greatest influence in issues of animal welfare and the use of animals in research (Sagoff, 1984).

Supporters of an ecocentric philosophy claim that the diversity of species, ecosystems, rivers, mountains and landscapes can have value in themselves, irrespective of the consequences on humans or other individuals of non-human species. All ecocentrics attach particular value to the diversity, dynamics and interactions within healthy ecosystems, but differ in their views on the cause of and proper solutions to modern environmental problems. Callicott (1979, 1989) and Næss (1974) both see the Western, instrumental view of nature as a main source of environmental problems. Ecofeminists suggest the problem lies in the history of male dominance and sexist oppression of females (Warren, 1990); others that it stems from the social and economic structure of society (Bookchin, 1991). Many locate the source of the problem in the Judeo-Christian tradition, and, more specifically, in the Biblical quotation:

"Let us make man in our image, after our likeness: and let them have dominion over the fish of the sea and over the fowl of the air, and over the cattle, and over all the earth, and over every creeping thing that creepth upon the earth". (Genesis 1: 26-30)

All ecocentrics claim that mankind needs a radical change from an anthropocentric attitude of domination and exploitation of natural resources towards a greater respect for the integrity of nature (deep ecologists like Næss, are perhaps more radical than others). In evaluating actions, Callicot defends the land-ethic maxim of Aldo Leopold, "A thing is right when it tends to preserve the integrity, stability, and beauty of the biotic community; it is wrong when it tends otherwise" (Leopold, 1949). The general concern for the biotic and abiotic community as a whole leads to the alternative classification of the outlook as an "holistic" ethic (Sagoff, 1984).

In defence of anthropocentrism, both scientists and philosophers have argued that human interests can provide a powerful set of motives for protecting nature (Wilson, 1984; Sober, 1986). William Frankena suggests that only humans are capable of "valuing" in an ethical sense (1973; 1979). In reply to Leopold and Callicott anthropocentrics ask: who is to answer the question of when a biotic community is stable and beautiful? Can such counsel ever express more than the ecological interests of humans and the species they most closely identify with? (Fritzell, 1987).

4.2   *Who has moral standing? Demarcation between humans and other organisms*

The question of who or what has moral status, and why, can have a strong influence on the way we balance human and environmental effects. As noted earlier, both utilitarians and deontologists have argued that moral standing should not be restricted to humans, and have suggested a number of different reasons for awarding moral significance. Singer's criterion of sentience only encompasses vertebrates, whereas Taylor suggests that all living organisms are equal moral subjects (egalitarian biocentrism) since each has some goal to its existence (Taylor, 1986). Note that for any biocentric view, as soon as the ethically relevant factor for assigning moral standing diverges from the "speciesist" criterion of simply being human to some trait such as rationality, consciousness or sentience, one is faced the problem of how to deal with those members of the human species that, due to some force of circumstance (accidental or otherwise), might be considered to rank lower than the higher animals. One either extends the scope for moral standing to include some animals, excludes some humans, or reverts to the "species" criterion. Finally, the concern for the abiotic components of the environment in ecocentrism, together with the fact that most definitions of the environment in international legislation include man, biota, abiota and physical surroundings, raises the issue of how to deal with the abiotic (i.e., soil, rocks, water) in environmental protection.

Interestingly, the anthropocentric and the non-anthropocentric ethic tend to highlight both man's uniqueness and our oneness with nature. Humans are the only ethical animal, the only "valuer"; humans are responsible for environmental destruction unmatched by any other species, population growth a singularly human problem. Biology, evolutionary science and genetics have shown that humans are continuous with the rest of nature, "yet none of this scientific reasoning can guarantee that we will develop ethical concern or a proper relation to the biosphere, any more than the knowledge that other human beings are our genetic kin will prevent us from annihilating them in war" (Bradford, 1993). We may agree that humans have a responsibility not to damage the environment, but disagree on what measures are needed to correct human behaviour, and when intervention to protect the environment is necessary. In practice, the variety of cultural and religious beliefs in the way humans perceive nature, and the differences in opinions on what has moral standing and why, can have a strong influence on the question of what it is exactly we mean by harm.

4.3   Harms and values in radiation protection

Present ICRP recommendations deal almost exclusively with the evaluation and management of human exposures, the standard argument for such a stance being that limits on exposure of humans will usually entail sufficient protection to the environment [ICRP 60, section 16 (ICRP, 1991)]. To claim that limiting exposures to humans will ensure a sufficient level of protection to the environment is not valid. There are many cases, for example, marine discharges and geological disposal, where barriers mean that an ecosystem could be exposed to high levels of radiation before measurable doses were seen in humans. In the 1960s, even the operators of the Windscale plant took the trouble to evaluate the possible environmental impact of its radioactive discharges (Dunster, 1964, cited in Kershaw, Pentreath, Woodhead & Hunt, 1992).

No one disputes that exposure to radiation can cause *changes* in biota and the environment, but what many experts question is the long-term consequences of such doses. It is accepted that deterministic, stochastic and hereditary effects in plants, insects and animals, have been seen both in the laboratory and after serious accidents and that species can show large variations in radiological sensitivity (Polikarpov, 1998). Scientists have documented genetic mutations in rodents and birds following the Chernobyl accident (Ellegren, Lindgren, Primmer & Moller, 1997; Pomerantseva, Ramaiya & Chekhovich, 1997) and damage to pine trees in the Red Forest (Skuterud, Goltsova, Næumann, Sikkeland & Lindmo, 1994). Following the Kyshtym accident, pine forests were replaced by the more radiation-resistant birch, and some insects and mammals showed observable biological effects on a population level (JNREG, 1997). But scientists disagree over whether or not these changes reflect permanent or serious ecological damage – after all the forests grew back, the wildlife returned, and genetic change is not always a bad thing (Baker, Hamilton, VandenBussche, Wiggins, Sugg, Smith, *et al.*, 1996). Indeed, a devil's advocate could ask whether the ecological benefit of removing humans from the Chernobyl area might outweigh any radiation detriments. Those consequences deemed "harmful" depend on the level protection awarded to the various components of the environment (individual, population, species, ecosystem). This in turn depends on the moral standing of those components.

The regulation of human exposure to radiation takes effects on individuals very seriously. Management of environmental hazards tends to disregard low rates of stochastic effects, focusing instead on the risk of harm to populations. In this respect, most (anthropocentric) environmental risk managers make a clear moral distinction between human and non-human species: individual humans matter; individual animals tend not to. The types of radiation exposure that result in observable (and probably, therefore, unacceptable) damage on a population level are thought to be far higher than the mSv levels at which intervention to protect humans takes place. While this might be true for mortality, however, it need not be the case for other biological endpoints such as reproductive ability and genetic effects. In some cases, such as for endangered species, effects on the individual are deemed to matter – even if not quite as much as for individual humans. Of course the variety of non-anthropocentric views may offer quite different interpretations and explanations on this last point. Some might be offended by the mere presence of man-made radionuclide in the environment, irrespective of any discernible effect on humans or biota.

To conclude, supporters of both anthropocentric and non-anthropocentric ethics can agree that harms to non-human populations should be avoided. They may disagree on the level of population change that can be accepted, and which populations should be considered the most important to protect. Deriving value from human preferences might cause harm to one species (e.g., pandas) more reprehensible than others (e.g., earthworms). Likewise all viewpoints could find specific cases where the individual would be the appropriate level of protection: the anthropocentric and ecocentric may focus on endangered species or habitats; the biocentric on certain individuals as having value in themselves. Both the anthropocentric and ecocentric may find it necessary to also address changes in the abiotic environment, i.e. increased concentrations of radionuclides in soil, water and air. Anthropocentric support for such views may arise from aesthetics or a wish to "preserve" "pristine" environments such as the Arctic; ecocentric support from the inherent value of all components of the ecosystem. In summary, population effects can be an appropriate focus for environmental protection from ionising radiation, but not at the exclusion of effects on individuals, ecosystems or even the abiotic environment itself.

4.4 *Compatibility with other Systems of Protection*

Any framework on protection of the environment from radiation should be compatible with systems for other environmental stressors. However, it is important to be aware that this area of law is under continuing development. There is a general world-wide consensus on the issue of human rights (even though there is not total agreement on how those principles might be applied in practice), which in some respects simplifies management of human radiation exposures. We have not reached anything like the same level of agreement on environmental principles, even though progress is ongoing and highly pertinent. Nevertheless, the history of environmental protection and legislation illustrates three points to bear in mind when considering protection of the environment from radiation. First, environmental protection is a relatively new type of legislation and one that is still undergoing development. Second, the issue is global, is deemed important by both governments and the public and has stimulated action on an international scale. Third, practical solutions are not without conflicts and controversy. Not withstanding these difficulties, examples of environmental law can be found in the national laws of every country. Although their scope and detail can vary considerably, progress during the last 30 years has led to a certain amount of agreement on what we mean by environment and its protection and which principles should guide that protection. At present the only part of the environment explicitly considered for protection from ionising radiation is man.

5.   How can ethics help?

Difficulties in defining a valuation for the environment include fundamental questions such as what exactly constitutes harming the environment and how the environment should be valued. Both of these, typically philosophical, problems arise in assessments of any environmental pollutant. Although philosophers might disagree about the *way* in which the environment should be valued, almost all philosophers would agree that damage to the environment should *matter* in risk assessment. Furthermore, most people would agree that harms caused by exposure of non-human species to radiation should carry weight in cost benefit analysis – this is because the species has value in itself and/or because of the potential consequences for future human generations.

It would be naive to expect radiation protection practitioner to resolve such fundamental problems within environmental philosophy, yet it is important that any framework developed should be flexible enough to incorporate both anthropocentric and ecocentric values. Although humans (as do all other organisms) use the environment instrumentally simply to survive, that does not preclude allocation of intrinsic value to biota, the abiotic environment or ecosystems as a whole. To be successful, and broadly justifiable in practice, environmental policy needs to consider both issues (Shrader-Frechette, 1991; Rolston, 1991).

It is important that ethics is seen as a tool rather than a burden in policy making. Because there are no easy answers to ethical dilemmas, it is necessary that any system of protection is sufficiently flexible to allow such conflicts to be addressed. With respect to environmental issues, different societies have different concepts of nature and its worth, and a comprehensive policy needs to be able to acknowledge, respect and protect this diversity in beliefs. Ethical evaluation can be valuable both in identifying controversies and in forcing decision makers to address the issues. Showing that decision makers are aware of, and have considered, such conflicts is an important step in making ethical issues transparent in policy making.

Ethicists put great weight on "treating like cases equally". In this respect, protecting the environment from the potential for radiation to cause harm will need to be put into context with the risks from other environmental pollutants and detriments. Unless there are clear, morally relevant grounds, radiation damage should not be treated differently than other hazards. Also, policy makers need to focus on considerations such as: who is involved in the decision making process; how to balance harms and benefits; and, ensuring that suitable alternatives have been considered. Finally, ethical evaluation extends the issue of whether a risk is acceptable, into dimensions that go beyond its probability of harm; ethical risk management asks questions other than those connected simply to radiation dose and its consequential cost to humans.

References

Amiro, B., Avadhanula, R., Johansson, G., Larsson, C-M., & Lüning, M. (eds.) 1996. *Protection of the Natural Environment: International Symposium on Ionising Radiation*. 2 vol, Swedish Radiation Protection Institute: Stockholm. pp1-434, 435-745.

Baker, R.J., Hamilton, M.J., VandenBussche, R.A., Wiggins, L.E., Sugg, D.W., Smith, M.H., Lomakin, M.D., Gaschak, S.P., Bundova, E.G., Rudenskaya, G.A., & Chesser, R.K. 1996. Small mammals from the most radioactive sites near the Chernobyl nuclear reactor power plant. *Journal of Mammalogy*, *77*, 155-170.

Beauchamp, T. & Childress, J. 1989. *Principles of Medical Ethics*. Oxford University Press: New York.

Bentham, J. 1789. *Introduction to the Principles of Morals and Legislation*. Chapter 17, Sect. 1. (1948, Hafner: New York).

Bentham, J. 1824. *Anarchical Fallicies*, Art. ii. (in: Collected works of Jeremy Bentham, 1983) Clarendon Press: London.

Bradford, G. 1993. Toward a deep social ecology. In: *Environmental Philosophy* (eds Zimmerman, M.E., Callicott, J.B., Sessions, G., Warren, K.J., Clark, J.) Prentice-Hall: New Jersey. pp. 418-437.

Bookchin, M. 1991. *The Ecology of Freedom*, 2nd Edition, Black Rose Books: Montreal.

Bookchin, M. 1993. *What is Social Ecology?* In: *Environmental Philosophy* (eds Zimmerman, M.E., Callicott, J.B., Sessions, G., Warren, K.J., Clark, J.) Prentice-Hall: New Jersey. pp. 354-373.

Callicott, J.B. 1979. Elements of an environmental ethic: moral considerability and the biotic community, *Environmental Ethics*, *1*, 71-81.

Callicott, B. 1989. *In Defense of the Land Ethic*. State University Press of New York: Albany.

Dunster, H.J., Garner, R., Howells, H., & Wix, L.F.U. 1964. Environmental monitoring associated with the discharge of low activity radioactive waste from the Windscale works to the Irish Sea. *Health Physics*, *10*, 353-362.

Ellegren, H., Lindgren, G., Primmer, C.R., & Moller, A.P. 1997. Fitness loss and germline mutations in barn swallows breeding in Chernobyl, *Nature*, *389*, 593-596.

Frankena, W.K. 1973. *Ethics*. Prentice-Hall: Englewood Cliffs.

Frankena, W.K. 1979. Ethics and the Environment. In: *Ethics and Problems of the Environment*, University of Notre Dame Press: Notre Dame.

Fritzell, P.A. 1987. The conflicts of ecological conscience. In: *Companion to a Sand County Almanac* (J.B. Callicott, ed.) University of Winsconsin Press: Madison.

Goodpaster, K. 1978. On being morally considerable, *Journal of Philosophy, 75*, 308-325.

Griffin, J. 1992. The human good and the ambitions of consequentialism. *Social Philosophy and Policy*, *9*, 118-132.

Hardin, R. 1988. *Morality within the Limits of Reason*, University of Chicago Press: Chicago.

Hare, R.M. 1952. *The Language of Morals*. Oxford University Press: Oxford.

Hare, R.M. 1982. Ethical Theory and Utilitarianism, In: *Utilitarianism and Beyond*. (A. Sen and B. Williams eds), Cambridge University Press, Cambridge.

Hobbes, T. 1651. *Leviathan*. (editor C.B MacPherson, 1982), Penguin Classics: London.

ICRP. 1991a. 1990 Recommendations of the International Commission on Radiological Protection. *Annals of the ICRP*, Pub. 60. Pergamon Press: Oxford.

JNREG (Joint Norwegian Russian Expert Group) 1997. Sources Contributing to Radioactive Contamination of the Techa River and areas surrounding the Mayak Production Association, Urals, Russia. JNREG: Østerås. (IBSN 82-993079-6-1).

Kovel, J. 1993. The marriage of radical ecologies. In: *Environmental Philosophy* (eds Zimmerman, M.E., Callicott, J.B., Sessions, G., Warren, K.J., Clark, J.) Prentice-Hall: New Jersey. pp. 406-417.

Kant, E. 1781 *The Critique of Pure Reason,* (trans. N.K. Smith) MacMillian: London, 1933.

Kant, E. 1785. *Groundwork of the Metaphysic of Morals* (trans. M. Gregor) Cambridge Texts in the History of Philosophy, Cambridge University Press: Cambridge.

Kershaw, P.J., Pentreath, R.J., Woodhead, D.S., & Hunt, G.J. 1992. *A Review of Radioactivity in the Irish Sea: A report prepared for the Marine Monitoring Management Group.* Aquatic Environment Monitoring Report 32, MAFF Directorate of Fisheries Research: Lowestoft.

Leopold, A. 1949. *A Sand County Almanac* (2nd ed. 1977), Oxford University Press. See also Callicott, J.B. (ed.) 1987. *A Companion to A Sand County Almanac*, University of Wisconsin, Madison.

MacIntyre, A. 1983. Utilitarianism and cost benefit analysis. in: *Ethics and the Environment*, (eds. D. Sherer and T. Attig), Prentice-Hall: Engelwood Clifts, N.J., p139-151.

Mill, J.S. 1871. *Utilitarianism.* (ed. R. Crisp, 1998) Oxford Philosophical Texts, Oxford University Press: London.

Norton, B. 1988. *Why Preserve Natural Variety?* Princeton University Press: Princeton.

Næss, A. 1974. *Økologi, Sammfunn og Livstil: Utkast til en Økosofi*, Universitetsforlaget: Oslo. (*Ecology, Community and Lifestyle: Outline of an Ecosophy*, trans. D. Rothenburg, 1990, Cambridge University Press: Cambridge).

Oughton, D.H. 2001. Ethical Evaluation of Radiation Risk, Ph.D. Thesis, Oslo University.

Oughton, D.H., & Bay, I. 2002. Ethical Considerations for Communication Strategies, *Strategy Report* FIKR-CT-2000-00018.

Pentreath, R.J. 1998. Radiological protection for the natural environment. *Radiation Protection Dosimetry*, *75*, 175-179.

Pentreath, R.J. 1999. A system for radiological protection of the environment: some initial thoughts and ideas. *Journal of Radiological Protection*, *19*, 117-128.

Polikarpov, G.G. 1998. Conceptual model of responses of organisms, populations and ecosystems to all possible dose rates of ionising radiation in the environment, *Radiation Protection Dosimetry*, *75*, 181-185.

Pomerantseva, M.D., Ramaiya, L.K., & Chekhovich, A.V. 1997. Genetic disorders in house mouse germ cells after the Chernobyl catastrophe. *Mutation Research – Fundamental and Molecular Mechanisms of Mutagenesis, 381*, 97-103.

Rawls, J. 1971. *A Theory of Justice*, Oxford University Press: London.

Regan, T. 1980. Animal rights, human wrongs, *Environmental Ethics*, 2, 99-120.

Regan, T., & Singer, P. 1976. *Animal Rights and Human Obligations* (Prentice-Hall: New Jersey).

Rolston, H. 1988. *Environmental Ethics*. Temple University Press: Philadelphia.

Rolston, H. III. 1991. Challenges in environmental ethics. *Ecology, Economics, Ethics: The Broken Circle*, Yale University Press: London.

Rousseau, J-J. 1755. *A Discourse on the Origin of Inequality*.

Rousseau, J-J. 1762. *Social Contract*. (trans. M. Cranston, 1987), Penguin Classics: London.

Sagoff, M. 1984. Animal liberation and environmental ethics: bad marriage quick divorce, *Ossgood Hall Law Journal, 22*, 297-307.

Scheffler, S. (ed.) 1988. *Consequentialism and its Critics*. Oxford University Press: Oxford.

Scheffler, S. 1994. *The Rejection of Consequentialism*. (2nd edition) Clarendon Press: Oxford.

Sen, A., & Williams, B. (eds) 1982. *Utilitarianism and Beyond* 1982. Cambridge University Press: New York.

Shrader-Frechette, K.S. 1991. *Risk and Rationality,* Univ. California Press: Berkeley.

Singer, P. 1991. *Animal Liberation: A new ethics for our treatment of animals* (2nd Edition). Thorsons: London.

Singer, P. 1993 *Practical Ethics*. (2nd ed) Cambridge University Press: Cambridge.

Skuterud, L., Goltsova, N.I., Næumann, R., Sikkeland, & T., Lindmo, T. 1994. Histological changes in *Pinis sylvestris* L. in the near-zone around the Chernobyl power plant. *Science of the Total Environment, 157*, 387-397.

Sober, E. 1986. Philosophical problems for environmentalism, In: *The Preservation of Species: The Value of Biological Diversity*, Princeton University Press: Princeton, pp. 180-188.

Sterba, J.T. 1994. Reconciling anthropogenic and nonanthropogenic environmental ethics, *Environmental Values, 3*, 229-244.

Taylor, P. 1986. *Respect for Nature.* Princeton University Press: Princeton.

Thomson, J.J. 1986. *Rights, Restitution, and Risk* (Harvard University Press: Cambridge, Massachusetts.

Warren, K.J. 1990. The power and the promise of ecological feminism. *Environmental Ethics, 12, 125-146.*

Williams, B. 1988. Consequentialism and integrity, In *Consequentialism and its Critics* (ed. S. Scheffler), Oxford University Press: Oxford.

Wilson, E.O. 1984. *Biophilia* Cambridge University Press: Cambridge.

STRATEGIES FOR THE PROTECTION OF THE ENVIRONMENT FROM OTHER HAZARDS

Kenneth Ruffing

Deputy Director, Environment Directorate, OECD

Strategies for the protection of the environment from radiological hazards may benefit from a consideration of risk management strategies applied in other areas. This paper attempts to do that with respect to the way the OECD has addressed these issues. The paper briefly describes the approach developed within the OECD on harmonisation and common approaches to chemicals risk management, related work by the Organisation on major industrial accidents and natural disasters, and places the relationship of chemical and radiological risk management in the context of the OECD Environmental Strategy for the First Decade of the Twenty-first Century.

Harmonisation and common approaches to chemicals risk management

Context

Our society's increasing dependence on chemicals is a relatively recent phenomenon. The chemicals industry today is a US$ 1.5 trillion global industry, nearly four times as big as it was 25 years ago. World-wide, the industry employs over 10 million people. The chemicals industry in OECD Member countries accounts for 78% of world-wide production. Chemicals and related products represent 9% of total global trade, and they make up 7% of global income.

Risks

While chemicals are indispensable in daily life, they can also pose risks to human health and to the environment. Examples of chemicals which are of concern are metals like lead, cadmium and mercury; the Persistent Organic Pollutants (POPs); tri-butyltin anti-fouling agents; carcinogenic azo-dyes and a number of chemicals with endocrine disrupting effects. Exposure of man and/or the environment to hazardous chemicals can occur during their manufacturing, storage, transport, use and/or disposal, and if the risks resulting from these exposures are not managed adequately human health and/or the environment can be seriously affected. All stakeholders involved with chemicals issues – governments, industries, trade unions, environmental citizens organisations and consumer groups – agree that chemical risks need to be managed, preferably by preventing these risks in the first place.

Management of risks

The chemicals industry is now in a period of strong globalisation and the manufacture and the use of chemicals is expanding rapidly outside the OECD. Increased trade liberalisation within the framework of the World Trade Organisation and regional agreements will undoubtedly lead to further growth in the trade of chemicals because tariffs will be decreasing across the globe. Chemical safety regulations are essential for human health and environmental protection, but if they are not harmonised internationally, they may become impediments to trade because they could function as non-tariff barriers. By promoting development of high quality regulations, which minimise unnecessary differences among countries, a win-win situation for health, environment and trade can be created. By managing chemical risks adequately and efficiently, the objectives of sustainable development with respect to chemical safety (UNCED's Agenda 21, chapter 19) will be achieved and global production and trade will continue to grow, but not at the expense of human health and the environment.

OECD's role

The main focus of work in OECD on chemicals is harmonisation of the chemical control approaches of Member countries while ensuring a high level of health and environmental protection. Through harmonisation, duplicative activities for government and industry related to pre-manufacturing or pre-marketing notification or registration of chemicals, and the creation of non-tariff trade barriers can be avoided. The Chemicals Programme also helps Member countries by organising burden sharing for the testing and assessment of chemicals, using harmonised methodologies. By working co-operatively in OECD, Member countries therefore benefit from increased efficiency in their own chemical safety programmes. According to a conservative estimate presented in a 1998 OECD Report, the work of the OECD Chemicals Programme currently leads to savings for governments and industry of at least US$ 50 million per year.

What aspects are harmonised?

Overall approach to chemicals management

In OECD countries (and increasingly in non-OECD countries) a science-based, rules based management approach is followed in which government and industry have the main responsibilities, while involving other stakeholders. This process includes:

- collection/generation (mainly through testing) of effects-related and exposure-related data, mainly by the industry;

- assessment (based on these data) of human health and environmental hazards and exposures;

- assessment of the risks by determining the probability that the hazards will occur;

- consideration of the need for risk management based on the outcome of the risk assessment, and development of risk management options, if appropriate;

- evaluation of the socio-economic impacts of the risk management options; and

- implementation of the risk management actions decided upon.

Harmonisation of testing and assessment

A prerequisite for a science-based process to manage the risks of chemicals to work well is the availability of adequate safety data. For new chemicals and pesticides notification/registration procedures exist involving the provision by industry of a package of safety related data. Hazard and risk assessments are made based on the information provided to government before manufacturing or marketing. For chemicals already on the market (existing chemicals) the lack of essential safety data is a problem with respect to making appropriate assessments and taking the necessary risk management decisions. For this reason a number of countries have decided that new and existing chemicals should be subject to registration. In as far as the data notification requirements and the test and assessment methods are harmonised, the data developed is mutually acceptable and can be shared.

Mutual acceptance of data

Three OECD Council Decisions related to MAD comprise an internationally-agreed system which helps to underpin national technical regulations in the area of acceptance of safety data for chemicals assessment. By establishing the basis for harmonised national policies for data acceptance (*1981 Council Decision on the Mutual Acceptance of Data in the Assessment of Chemicals* and *1989 Council Decision-Recommendation on Compliance with Good Laboratory Practice*) and developing and maintaining internationally-agreed instruments for their implementation (Test Guidelines, GLP Principles and Compliance Monitoring Procedures), OECD has created among its Member countries a standards-based system which meet the main WTO (TBT) objectives of transparency and avoidance of unnecessary barriers to trade being created by technical regulations. By opening up this system to non-OECD countries through the *1997 Council Decision on Adherence of Non-Member Countries to the OECD Council Acts related to the Mutual Acceptance of Data*, the system has become in principle accessible to all WTO Members.

Harmonisation of management

The data developed and assessed is the basis for decisions made on risk management actions. In cases where satisfactory information is lacking, a number of countries are inclined to follow a precautionary approach and make management decisions which are likely to err on the side of safety. Although to a lesser extent than data development and assessment, risk management is also harmonised in OECD countries as far as possible in order to create a level playing field and maintain high environmental standards. Approaches to supporting decision making are shared. Development of common approaches to life cycle management of chemicals with respect to their manufacture, storage, transport, use and disposal is an overall goal of the Chemicals Programme.

Major industrial accidents and natural disasters

Potential environmental impacts are, of course, not only – or mainly – associated with the high probability/low impact events associated with the normal course of operations in the production, storage, transport, use and disposal of hazardous substances or products that contain them. They are also associated, especially in the consciousness of the general public, with the low probability/high impact events, such as major industrial accidents and natural disasters.

While not currently on the agenda of the Environmental Policy Committee, the OECD has developed a guidance framework for dealing with such events, mainly in the 1980s. The framework includes a recommended set of measures, including regulatory and economic instruments aimed at:

a)   prevention and mitigation of potential damages;

b)   emergency preparedness;

c)   emergency action; and

d)   damage repair, including restoration of ecosystems.

The framework also includes recommendations on financial responsibility based on the application of the Polluter-Pays Principle (PPP), distinguishing among the use of:

a)   liability and compensation insurance;

b)   national budgetary allocations;

c)   cost recovery, especially of the public administration costs of risk management; and

d)   international co-operation.

In 1989, the OECD Council adopted a Recommendation concerning the Application of the Polluter-Pays Principle to Accidental Pollution (7 July 1989 – C(89)88/Final) which lays out a set of *Guiding Principles* incorporating most of the framework mentioned above. One aspect of the PPP concerns arrangements for the distribution of financial responsibilities among countries in the event of accidents having transboundary impacts. This was applied to the case of oil spills in 1981 when the OECD Council adopted a Recommendation concerning Certain Financial Aspects of Actions by Public Authorities to Prevent and Control Oil Spills (28 April 1981 – C(81)32/Final).

The relationship of risk management to sustainable development: A comparison of chemical and radiological risk management

Objectives

The objectives for enhancing cost-effective and operational environmental policies in the context of sustainable development set out in the *OECD Environmental Strategy for the first decade of the 21st Century* are being taken increasingly into account in assessment and management of both chemical and radiological risks. In the following tables some of the characteristics of the principles for radiation protection and chemicals safety are described in relation to these objectives.

A.   *Maintaining the integrity of ecosystems through the efficient management of natural resources*

This objective deals with maintaining the integrity of ecosystems, staying within their capacity as sources and sinks. Measures include intemalisation so that prices reflect the full external costs of natural resource use.

Radiation	Chemicals
Sink capacity: For releases of carbon-14, a balance between supply to the environment and removal has been the basis for establishing upper limits for the installed capacity of nuclear power according to Swedish regulations (SS1 FS 1991:5, see www.ssi.se).	Sink capacity: The concept of critical loads has been applied to find tolerable pressure on the environment. It has, however, been questioned whether there is not a sliding scale without clear threshold, requiring value judgement in establishing the critical load (Skeffington 1999)
Sink capacity: The natural flow of radioactive substances has been proposed as a yardstick for allowing much smaller long-term releases of radioactive substances to the environment (Bergman *et al*., 1987).	Sink capacity: According to the same criterion, severe restriction on the uses of several metals would be required (compare above: Basic principles of chemical safety, Exposures and effects).
	Sink capacity: Effects on other organisms than man, in particular reproductive effects, are common in the assessment of risks from chemicals but scenarios are crude.
Source capacity: The radiation consequences of using up all available uranium for nuclear power have been calculated and found tolerable (NEA 2000).	Source capacity: The health and environmental consequences of continuing to mobilise substances at rates an order of magnitude higher than the natural ones have hardly been discussed. Chemical safety scenarios in technical guidance documents with the EU deal with local and regional exposures but no tools are available for dealing with the overlap from all sources in the world over long periods of time.
Internalisation of health and environmental costs: In the nuclear fuel cycle, costs for waste management (waste fee) and for potential accidents (insurance) are internalised; these are partly related to radiation protection requirements.	
Internalisation of health and environmental costs: For radioactive releases, mitigating action is required to strike a balance between the internal costs of mitigation and the external costs of health and environmental effects (the ALARA principle).	

B.   De-coupling environmental pressures from economic growth

This objective addresses consumption and production patterns. Increasing the availability of product and production process information should facilitate consumer choices. Again external costs should internalise. Resource efficiency and too high growth in production and consumption should be addressed. Regulatory as well as voluntary measures should be applied. The sectors should integrate environmental concerns in their strategies, and particular attention should be paid to the agriculture, energy and transport sectors.

Well established measures for both radiation protection and chemical safety include licensing for the most hazardous practices, consideration of materials efficiency and waste minimisation, including reuse and recycling of materials, and more or less strict application of the Polluter Pays Principle. Mathematical modelling is extensively used both for dispersion of substances in the environment and for effects from ingested substances or incurred doses.

Radiation	Chemicals
Practice/Intervention: Control of new practices from the beginning is distinguished from intervention in existing situations, and exposure quantities accordingly defined (existing dose vs. additional dose) (ICRP 1999).	Practice/Intervention: Control of the marketing of substances that are new to the market is distinguished from control of the marketing of substances that exist in the market.
General consumption: Radioactive products for general consumption, such as smoke detectors, are extremely strictly limited (NEA 1985).	General consumption: An Integrated Product Policy is to be published by the EU in the spring of 2001 (http://europa.eu.int/comm/environment/ipp/home.htm).
Use patterns: The emphasis when deciding on restrictions is on risks, not inherent hazards. This means that expected exposures almost always form part of the background factors for decisions on protective measures.	Consumption patterns: The increasing volumes of chemicals in combination with their inherent hazards call for new strategies. There is room to complement the present direction to limit the inherently most hazardous chemicals by promoting strongly increased resource efficiency to reduce volumes significantly.
Sector integration: The role of nuclear energy in the energy sector has been thoroughly addressed (NEA 2000).	Sector integration: This is being elaborated in the EU as a high priority for sustainable development.
Product information ionising radiation: Strict rules including labelling apply for transport of radioactive materials (http://www.iaea.org/ns/rasanet/programme/radiationsafety.htm#I.3%20Transport%20Safety) and for use of radiation in the workplace.	Product information: The safety system has as a cornerstone standardised criteria for providing information about hazards, for instance hazards to the aquatic environment, carcinogenicity or reproductive toxicity; standardised testing to establish accordance with the criteria; standardised labelling and symbols to convey judgements about test results.
Product information for lasers: The basic safety system relies on classification and labelling of lasers.	Notification to importing countries: A global convention (http://irptc.unep.ch/pic/) requires prior notification of importing countries for a few dozen hazardous substances.

Radiation	Chemicals
Choice of practice: One of three cornerstones for ionising radiation is Justification of practice: No practice should be adopted unless it produces sufficient benefit to the exposed individual or to society to offset the radiation detriment it causes.	Choice of chemical: The principle of comparative assessment is often applied: if possible, hazardous chemicals should be replaced by less hazardous ones. This leaves a lot of details in risk management to various actors involved with chemicals.
Balancing protection and resource demand: One of three cornerstones for ionising radiation is Optimisation of protection: The magnitude of the individual doses, the number of people exposed, and the likelihood of incurring exposures where these are not certain to be received should all be kept as low as reasonably achievable, economic and social factors being taken into account. This leaves a lot of details in risk management to various actors involved with radiation For the decision making, rules of thumb have been developed for the trade-off between costs of further protection and further reduction of radiation doses. The basis for the trade-off of radiation doses is the collective dose, i.e. the sum of the average doses in a population. The individual doses may also be involved in the trade-off A monetary value, a, is assigned to the unit collective dose. If the cost of further collective dose reduction by one unit exceeds a, then the protection level is beyond the optimum. This may still have to be accepted to keep individual doses below the basic dose limits.	Life cycle analysis: Increasingly, the life cycle of practices is reviewed to ensure that risks from e.g. mining, oil extraction or waste management are not overlooked. This may include the study of alternative methods to obtain a given function, say the use of irradiation, natural fungi or chemical pesticides to reduce the amount of weeds in agricultural soils.
Voluntary commitments: The nuclear industry in applying optimisation often gives greater weight to protection than minimum requirements.	Voluntary commitments: The chemical industry has an extensive commitment world wide called Responsible Care (http://www.icca-chem.org/), incorporating a responsibility also for what their customers do (Product Stewardship).

C.   *Improving information for decision making: Measuring progress through indicators*

Interim and long-term quantitative targets should be set for suitable indicators, and progress towards these targets should be monitored. Environmental information should be accessible for all citizens.

Radiation	Chemicals
Indicators: Indicators have been developed to enable the aggregation of the dose to an individual from different sources (e.g. effective dose) and to a group of individuals (collective dose) (ICRP 1991).	Indicators: Indicators of progress are poorly developed. The total amount of pesticides sold is widely used, without risk weighting. Indices are being developed, e.g. concerning the use of pesticides (http: //www. oecd.org/ehs/pest/PEST _RI.pdf). A few indicator substances are widely monitored, e.g. dioxins and polychlorinated biphenyls, in a few organisms, e.g. in marine animals.
Environmental quality: Objectives have been set to be compared with hypothetical future average exposures from all sources (ICRP 1991); based on harm to humans.	Environmental quality: Objectives are being proposed for substance levels in specific media, e.g. for water two or three dozen substances are likely to be covered (http://europa.eu.int/eur lex/en/com/pdf/2000/en_500PC0047.pdf); based on harm to a few specific indicator organisms, mainly from local exposure scenarios.
Environmental information: Internationally compiled state-of-the-art reports are published on sources and effects (UNSCEAR 2000). Much of the detailed basic information is also published nationally, e.g. for releases from nuclear power installations.	Environmental information: Internationally compiled state-of-the-art reports for specific substances often contain information on exposures and effects (see above: Basic principles of chemical safety: Exposures and effects). Making release information available is part of industry's voluntary commitment Responsible Care. In a few countries, and for a limited number of substances, emission registers have been established, sometimes call Pollutant release and transfer registers (PRTR, see http://www. oecd.org/ehs/prtr/index.htrn). In a few countries, registers on chemical products entering the market are available, covering tens of thousands of products (lubricants, paints, glues etc) and many thousand substances (Kraft 1999).

D.   *The social and environmental interface: Enhancing human health, the quality of life,*
        environmental justice and democracy

In addition to the already extensively studied economic/environmental and economic/social interfaces, the social/environmental interface should be studied. This includes effects of environmental degradation on human health, civic society involvement in environmental issues, and the relation between environmental policies and social consequences such as employment, social inclusion and community development.

Radiation	Chemicals
Effects on human health: The widely used indicators such as effective dose and collective dose are designed to protect human health (ICRP 1991). For new practices, the system has generally been effective. For intervention in already existing situations, there still remains much to be done, e.g. for radon in homes.	Effects on human health: There is little overview of long-term human health effects, even those incurred from new substances which are permitted on the market. There is reason for concern about e.g. children's health (see above:
The system is designed to account for:	Basic principles of chemical safety: Exposures and effects).
• all exposures, in principle over all distances;	For limited practices good health protection is ensured, such as food additives or pharmaceuticals, and some substances in occupational health.
• and all times;	
• potential exposures which are not certain to occur;	
• all sources, e.g. nuclear power and the use of radioactive substances in hospitals; a margin of exposure is allotted to allow for overlapping exposures;	
• the most highly exposed individuals, represented by a hypothetical critical group.	

E.   *Global environmental interdependence: Improving governance and co-operation.*

This objective deals with the management of environmental effects of globalisation through improved national and international environmental governance, including the incorporation of environmental concerns into international economic and financial institutions and agreements. Corporations are encouraged to adopt higher standards of performance through non-binding instruments. Technical cooperation for policy and institutional frameworks in developing and transition countries is important.

Radiation	Chemicals
Global co-operation: A peer-established body (International Commission on Radiological Protection) recommends widely accepted data and management practices for ionising radiation. See also above under Dealing with lack of knowledge, complexity and diversity of values.	Global co-operation: Intergovernmental bodies co-ordinate international work: IFCS and IOMC (see above: Basic principles of chemical safety: Historic development). See also above under Dealing with lack of knowledge, complexity and diversity of values.
International treaties: Many treaties at the regional or global level, e.g. on radioactive waste and nuclear safety. Often synoptic in character, e.g. agreement at the expert level on transboundary radiation exposure (IAEA 1985): • policies and criteria for protection of populations outside national borders should be at least as stringent as those for the population within the country of release; • in any case, a minimum value (3000 USD at 1983 prices) should be applied for unit collective doses (in mansievert) appearing outside the national border.	International treaties: Many treaties at the regional or global level, e.g. on chemical waste, and limitation of transboundary releases. Generally incremental in character, defining e.g. agreed percentage reductions in releases.
Export responsibility: Materials that could be used for production of nuclear weapons are subject to export restrictions.	Export responsibility: Materials that could be are used for production of chemical weapons subject to export restrictions. A global convention (http://irptc.unep.ch/pic/) requires prior notification of importing countries for a few dozen hazardous substances.

Conclusions

The practices involving radiation protection and chemical safety should concur with sustainable development objectives. The purposes of radiation protection and chemical safety are to ensure that protection of health and the environment is given sufficient weight when the balance is sought between the social, economic and environmental dimensions of sustainable development.

In radiation protection, control of new practices from the beginning (prevention) is distinguished from intervention in existing situations. In both radiation protection and chemical safety, control of practices as well as interventions is used, but radiation protection has come much further in controlling practices, with e.g. due regard taken to the capacity of sinks to absorb pollution. For nuclear power, costs of environmental pollution, waste management and accidents are to a high degree internalised, partly following pressure form the radiation protection community, whereas there are only limited examples of the corresponding for chemicals. Important facets of chemical safety include attempts at systematically dealing with effects on other organisms than man, and in particular, the importance of reproductive disturbances is interesting as a lead to potential radiation effects on the environment. In chemical safety, there seems to be wider acknowledgement of the importance of allowing for a diversity of value judgements in risk management. Export of "strong" chemical sources is regulated whereas the corresponding does not hold for strong radiation sources.

Modern radiation protection and chemical safety are often highly complex and require the management of uncertainties. Reduction of such complexity to simpler rules of thumb, which can be applied by a wide range of stakeholders, will be increasingly important. Securing social consent to resolve important issues of importance for social and economic aspects of sustainable development is a never-ending task. It must take due account of environmental and health aspects such as those of radiation protection and chemical safety. Their centralised and decentralised systems must increasingly be supplemented by systems which are non-centralised in character.

EXPECTATIONS FOR THE PROTECTION OF THE ENVIRONMENT: ARE EXPOSURES IMPORTANT?

Simon Carroll

Adviser, Political and Science Division, Greenpeace International

Radiological protection standards have been established with the principal objective of seeking to provide appropriately safe conditions for activities involving human exposure. In this context ICRP-26 (1977) asserted the Commission's belief that, if man is protected to this level, then other "living things" are also likely to be sufficiently protected. Just over a decade ago the ICRP (*Publication No. 60, 1990*) modified the 1977 view to take into account the possibility that non-human species "might be harmed". At the same time, ICRP asserted also that the standard of environmental control needed to protect man to the degree currently thought desirable will ensure that other species are not put at risk. Even if there was some harm caused, whole species would not be endangered nor would an imbalance be created between species.

It is important to recognise that there are value judgements and assumptions embedded in these statements, certainly with regard to the environment but also in the radiological protection of humans. In applying the principles of radiological protection in practice, further value judgements are employed.

In seeking to develop an approach towards radiological protection of the environment it is necessary to recognise and question these and other value judgements and assumptions, and to clearly define the objectives being sought.

The "regulator's dilemma"

Immediately, some basic questions arise. How should basic principles be established? Should scientific efforts concentrate on examining dose-effect responses to radiological exposure of non-human biota or should they concentrate on gaining a better understanding of the degree and causes of radioactive contamination of the environment, or both? How important are assessments of exposures to non-human biota compared with, for example, the development and implementation of best management practices intended to reduce and eliminate the sources of radioactive contamination of the environment? Is there a need to draw a distinction between environmental assessments of ongoing practices, unplanned events and remedial measures?

For a regulator, I would suggest that the basic purpose of developing an approach to protection of the environment is to:

- provide information on which to base decisions relating to the future control of on-going activities;

- enable adaptations to "foreseen" emerging "issues", the original causes of which we have no effective control; and

- ensure that "best practice" is used with the overall objective of realising sustainable development.

In seeking to do so, I believe it is important to recognise that:

- **decisions** cannot be based on science alone (although science is an essential input); and

- getting the **questions** correct is as important as **finding** the "right" answers.

Essentially there are two basic options for science-informed regulatory approaches:

- **a risk-based approach**, which uses scientific information in attempts to arrive at system descriptions and predictions of effects which are as numerically accurate as possible, assuming that reliability of predictions can be increased progressively through reduction and elimination of uncertainties; and

- **a precautionary approach**, which uses scientific information in order to guide the development of preventive measures, recognising inherent uncertainties and limitations to knowledge and ensuring that regulatory measures err on the side of precaution rather than assumption.

It is important to note that both approaches rely on the provision of high-quality scientific information, and that they differ in the underlying philosophies governing its interpretation. The dilemma for the regulator arises in the decision that must be made in choosing between the two approaches. Should one choose a path defined by what is "believed to be known" or should one restrict the possible choices by an understanding of the limits to knowledge?

Limitations to a risk-based approach

Approaches based on the assessment and management of risk have received much attention in recent years, relying essentially on the application of techniques developed in engineering sciences to the forecasting of trends and impacts in incredibly more complex and much less well-defined natural systems – "ecosystems".

Risk-based approaches extend from the view that environmental risks can first be accurately quantified and subsequently managed in light of this information so as to make them "sustainable" and "acceptable" – either in absolute terms or relative to the benefits perceived to have been derived.

Scientific research undoubtedly has the ability to improve our understanding of ecosystems and their functioning, including the consequences of external stresses. Research into such areas therefore is clearly to be welcomed and encouraged. At the decision-making level, however, we need to be aware of the inherent limitations. All "scientific" determinations are bound by the largely arbitrary constraints of experimental design and the need to control, as far as possible, externalities.

Even an intricate experimental design is unlikely to address properties about which we remain ignorant. The inherent existence of a multitude of processes, networks and chains of causality within ecosystems will always be barriers to truly comprehensive description and prediction of ecosystem functions.

The implicit and operational limitations, uncertainties, and indeterminacies of the description of ecosystems, and interactions within them, can result in the transmission of substantial uncertainty and inaccuracy to the analysis of associated risk caused by the presence of external agents, including radionuclides, in the environment. Moreover, where verification of data provided is absent or incomplete, and I would suggest that this is the case for numerous cases of environmental contamination by radionuclides, these problems are clearly exacerbated. Where incomplete or inaccurate data were used as a basis for establishing the existing standards, these problems become self-reinforcing.

One example of the limited relevance of the value of such risk-based assessments in environmental management and policy making can be found in the debate concerning the dumping of radioactive waste at sea. At the request of the Contracting Parties to the Convention on the Prevention of Marine Pollution by Dumping of Wastes (London Convention, 1972), the IAEA provided a definition of high-level radioactive wastes or other radioactive matter unsuitable for dumping at sea and recommendations which should be taken into account when issuing special permits for dumping (IAEA Safety Series No. 78, IAEA, 1986 edition).

The quantitative Definition was derived using models recommended by GESAMP and a database established by the IAEA. It is based on the assumptions *inter alia* that dumping takes place in a single ocean basin of a volume $10^{17} m^3$ at a depth of at least 4000 metres at a rate of 10^8 kg per year and that this continues for 1000 years. The model assumed instantaneous release of radionuclides upon impact of waste packages with the ocean floor. The Definition was based on an annual "dose limit" for human individuals of 1 mSv per year applied to a critical group. The IAEA did note that this formula was not meant to imply that 1 mSv per year was an acceptable exposure to humans due to ocean dumping of radioactive waste. Rather the IAEA stated that it would be prudent to use a value substantially lower than 1 mSv per annum pending international accord on a dose upper bound for sea dumping.

So what happened? One Contracting Party to the London Convention continued to dump radioactive wastes at sea in ways not in accord with the definition and recommendations and only ceased these activities when they were made widely known publicly. The Contracting Parties to the London Convention collectively agreed to halt all dumping of radioactive waste at sea, taking into account a host of factors and recognising that the doses to individuals were not the main factor of concern and, in any case, there were significant uncertainties in the "science". The uncertainties were not only with respect to human exposures. It was recognised that possible environmental impacts had been studied much less intensively than human exposures and therefore there was relatively limited data available for a very limited number of species. Taking into account the limited knowledge and the inherent uncertainties, implicitly and explicitly Parties stated that considerations of "values" and "practices" were at least as relevant as "data" on doses in making the determination of whether dumping should be allowed to continue.

Advantages of a precautionary approach

It was recognition of substantial and, to a degree, irreducible limitations to scientific knowledge which lead initially to the formulation of a precautionary approach to environmental protection. The basic purpose of employing a precautionary approach is to enable decision-making where "information" is incomplete and therefore ignorance or incertitude is a "given".

Rather than implying that "nothing should ever be done" (as the Precautionary Principle is sometimes portrayed), a precautionary approach simply requires that:

- damage should preferably be prevented;

- decisions should be informed by scientific research;

- action to prevent harm is essential, even in the absence of proof of causality; and

- all activities should meet the requirement for progressive reduction of environmental burdens.

Since its origins, the Precautionary Principle has gained increasing acceptance as a fundamental guiding paradigm and it forms a central component of numerous national and international legislative frameworks on the protection of the environment.

One advantage of a precautionary approach is that it applies science in a less prescriptive manner whilst retaining the quality input to decision making as a guide to a policy decision. At the same time, it takes account of the fact that further scientific research and methods development are essential if we are to better elucidate mechanisms and become more effective at identifying, predicting and addressing environmental threats.

The key feature of such an approach is the recognition that the results of scientific research can only guide policy making, it cannot decide policy making in itself. It also recognises the limits to understanding and certitude. Lastly, it recognises that deferring decisions until such time as the implications of environmental impacts are better understood may be "irresponsible".

Expectations

If the new assessments underway to better understand environmental impacts of ionising radiation are to be useful, they must:

- provide useful information on which to base decisions relating to the future control of on-going activities;

- enable adaptations to "foreseen" emerging "issues", the original causes of which we have no effective control because we are left with a "legacy"; and

- ensure that "best practice" is used in making choices about possible future activities.

There is no doubt that gains in knowledge can be realised through new assessments on impacts of radiation on non-human biota, and such new information is to be welcomed.

However, if the management approaches generated by the new assessments are to be both useful and generally accepted, they must:

- take into account the uncertainties and knowledge gaps in the assessments, and also clearly state assumptions made (both in the design of the assessments and in the conclusions drawn from the studies);

- incorporate "values" as well as "science";

- take into account and incorporate knowledge gained and developments in environmental protection outside of the nuclear sector (both with respect to the conduct of scientific assessments as well as in adopting management approaches and goals); and

- be perceived as genuine management tools rather than justifications for protecting a specific established industry or practices.

In this context, a better understanding of exposures to non-human biota is useful but it is only one of many factors to be taken into consideration in seeking to develop an effective approach to ensure protection of the environment from ionising radiation.

RADIATION PROTECTION WITH RESPECT FOR NATURE, VIEWS FROM JAPAN

Kenzo Fujimoto

National Institute of Radiological Sciences, Japan

Introduction

Environmental problems due to radiation are presently found only in confined or contaminated areas due to accidents or relatively high radioactive releases from nuclear facilities and high-level radioactive waste depository sites. In the radiological protection system it has been assumed that there would be no harm to any species as long as the radiation is controlled to the degree for the safety to man. All other species and environment have been considered only with regards to the transfer of radionuclides to man. So far we have kept an anthropocentric view to the environment. We have placed human beings at the top of the hierarchy and have tried to control the environment, whilst endangering other species, for our own benefit. Since we have multiplied ourselves by the sacrifice of other creatures and expanded our activity extensively, we have become like cancer cells on the earth. Some of our activities have already been far beyond the capacity of nature for natural recovery. The examples are air pollution, water pollution and massive energy consumption. In some advanced countries local climates have been changed significantly due the intensive energy consumption. One typical example can be found in Kyoto. Katsura Rikyu was built from 1624-1663 as one of the villas of the Emperor in Kyoto. It was designed to show its beauty with snow cover. However, they seldom have snowfall in the urban area of Kyoto these days due to the greenhouse effect. If all the people on earth used the same amount of energy that is consumed by the average Japanese person, the earth would no longer be able to keep the energy balance any more. If we continue our activities based on the present anthropocentric, egoistic and vast desire of development, our natural environment could not be maintained in a healthy condition any more.

Review of present

Environmental conservation has been a recent movement in the world. However, there is no concrete consensus on the conservation approach. For the establishment of an environmental protection system we have to be liberated from the old self-bindings and stereotypical ideas, and change our present sense of values and morals. We have to consider the problems under the recognition of Spaceship Earth and with a longer time-scale. We have to abandon the anthropocentrism and respect the dignity of other living creatures. Some of these movements have already begun for the protection of experimental animals and the name change of pets to partners. However, we still discriminate due to skin colour, religion and gender. We have to cast aside these wrong concepts and abandon the selfishness as well as the anthropocentric eco-balance.

Balance of nature

We should be compassionate toward nature and have respect for nature. However, we should not run to an extreme that prevents us from eating any meat or giving up all civilised life. All the animals in nature live at the expense of other creatures. Humankind also lives by sacrificing other lives. Our living seems to be in conflict with environmental protection. This is our reality. We are not living by ourselves. Lions, for example, live by killing other animals for their food, but not for leisure. Their hunting does not cause damage to nature, rather control the number of food animals. All creatures are living within the balance of nature. This is the only way we can survive on the earth. Therefore, we have to conform to the providence of Mother Nature with the recognition that human beings are also one component in nature. And we have to search for the golden mean in nature.

New approach

Lets consider the golden mean that we should take in balance of nature. The golden mean is somewhere in the middle between no action and the extreme. Any action we take causes some burden to nature. Our harm to nature should be kept within the acceptable level. However, it is extremely difficult to determine the acceptable level for each action since we have limited knowledge to evaluate its impact in the ecosystem. Therefore, we may use other simple ways to estimate the acceptable level of nature. The level could be equivalent to the range of the fluctuation of radiation dose rate in nature. The radiation level in nature varies from time to time. Even the highest level of radiation found in the fluctuation could be understood as acceptable to nature. Other variations of radiation dose rate found among regions is larger than that of time difference. The regional difference can be used as the level of acceptable range. UNSCEAR report in the year 2000 shows dose distribution based on the measurements in 25 countries for outdoor absorbed dose rate in the air from terrestrial gamma radiation. The report shows the difference in gamma levels of around 1 mSv per year. There are other extreme cases that demonstrate the dose rate of more than 10 mSv in some areas. However, these higher values are not used here since we are pursuing the golden mean, but not the extreme. Alpha dose that can be found in the natural environment could be far larger than the gamma dose once the receptor size of creature is less than a few tens of micrometers. However, as the size increases the dose due to alpha rays decreases sharply and becomes smaller compared to the gamma dose as far as the average absorbed dose in tissue is concerned. Therefore, only the dose due to gamma rays is considered here as the acceptable range by nature.

Application

Not only do we need the numbers for environmental protection. We have to have a clear recognition of our position within nature for the reform of justification and optimisation. The basic understanding we have to realise in environmental protection is that all our activities could not be considered as natural. For example, the road that monkeys made could be considered to be natural. The monkey road could be recovered to be an original form once no monkeys use the road again. Ninja roads could also be considered to be like the monkey road. However, all other roads we made are not natural but artificial. The roads could not return to the original condition even though the roads are free from human impacts for a quite long time. We have to realize big harm of our action on nature. Therefore, we have to pay a lot of attention when we make some actions not to damage the nature and not to destroy it permanently. If it is unavoidable to harm the nature, we have to confine the damage as small as possible.

Based on these understandings and reformed attitude we can set a control level for radiation for practice taking into account the acceptable level mentioned before. The additional dose rate at the boundary of nuclear or radiation facilities should be below 1 mGy per year, regardless of the presence of people. Once the radioactivity are handled in the facility the releasing levels should be controlled by the limit described below. For natural radionuclides, normal ambient concentration in air or water would be the limit based on the natural fluctuation of concentration. For all artificial radionuclides the acceptable level to be release to the environment can be chosen based on the derived dose rate taking into account the accumulation in biota and abiota.

When damage occurred on the environment, such as contamination, the system of intervention is applied. The approach to the intervention and the practice is considerably different. For intervention there is a big difficulty for the trade-off between man and other species. When an intervention is implemented man will be exposed to radiation in order to reduce the exposure to other creatures. To overcome this difficulty, interventional situation could be considered with the analogy to natural disasters. When a volcano erupts and lava flows out of the volcano, large areas around the volcano could be damaged completely. Like the case of this natural disaster, when it is easy to recover the damage we should then restore it. If it is not easy, we have to confine the damage not to spread the damage outside.

Potential exposure might be another aspect to be covered in the frame of environmental protection. In the present radiological protection system potential exposure can be controlled by two ways. One is prevention, i.e., the reduction of occurrence probability of events that may cause or increase radiation exposures. The other is mitigation. That is the limitation and reduction of the exposures if any of these sequences do occur. For accident prevention for example in a depository facility, we have to recall that nothing could remain permanently in nature. The way nature prepares for the sustainability is the alternation of generations, i.e., a renewal process after a certain time period is programmed by nature for maintaining life. This is the way that we could imitate from nature to maintain certain facilities under control for a very long time.

You can find a good example in Ise Shrine in Japan. It is believed the shrine was founded about 2 000 years ago. About 1 300 years ago a system of relocation of the shrine every 20 years was established to ensure the technology transfer, and to maintain the worship of the shrine among people. The 20-year cycle is considered to be an appropriate time period at the time of 1 300 years ago for keeping the tradition of belief and techniques since the life span might be shorter than that of today. In 1993 the shrine was relocated for the 61st time. With this renewal system the shrine has been kept fresh for more than one thousand years. Learning from nature and Ise Shrine, we should understand nothing could remain forever. Therefore, the renewal system could be one of the options for long-term control of radioactive waste depository sites. This could reduce the occurrence probability of accident due to the loss of control or ageing of facilities. We can keep the high radioactive depository under the human control by rebuilding or relocating the facility with a certain time of period.

The other objective for potential exposure is mitigation. As one of suggestion for the mitigation, decentralisation of facilities might be a good option since the consequence of accident in one facility could be smaller compared to the centralised facility.

Summary

My new proposal was summarised below for the protection of environment based on the understanding that we can exist on earth only in the balance of nature. We must follow the providence of nature and attain the golden mean in nature. For justification and optimisation, any concrete idea has not been provided, but one of the approaches was shown in the present paper. We have to abandon anthropocentrism and change our sense of value and moral standards with the respect for nature. For practice, the dose limit at the boundary of facilities could be derived from the regional difference of dose rates in the world as an acceptable level to nature. The dose rate would be around 1 mGy per year. Release limit for radionuclides could be defined separately to natural and artificial nuclides. For natural radionuclides, normal ambient concentration can be used for the limit. For artificial radionuclides, the limit might be based on the derived dose rate taking into account the accumulation. For intervention, an analogical approach to natural disasters could be applied. When the situation is easy to recover, then it should be restored. In case it is not easy, then the damage should be confined not to spread outside. For potential exposure, two approaches are suggested for prevention and mitigation. Renewal system is proposed for prevention and decentralisation for mitigation.

A rigid number for the dose limit is shown in the present paper, as well as renewal or relocation for the radiation protection for environment. However, it is not necessary to take them as they are. For the practical application, definitely it requires some modification. Therefore, present suggestions should be taken as some hint for the establishment of radiation protection system for environment. Especially the suggested dose limit of 1 mGy per year should be taken as the lowest limit for the acceptable level to nature.

PANEL DISCUSSION*

Following a most interesting session of papers on present policies, ethical considerations, and possible rationales and expectations with regard to protection of the environment, most of this first panel discussion centred on the more basic issues of: why should society be worried about the environmental effects of radiation now, relative to all of the other environmental problems that we face; and why should the radiological protection community therefore need to consider the development of a new approach?

The views of the panel were that it was essential first to see this issue in its proper context, in that it was nowadays necessary to demonstrate that full concern was being paid to environmental matters resulting from human activities of any kind, regardless of whether the actual risk was large or small. Radiological protection therefore had to fit in with this modern pattern. But it was not necessary to treat it in isolation, or to try and be different. A large body of international legislation, agreements, and commitments already existed with respect to environmental protection in a general sense, and thus it was necessary and sensible to work within such frameworks – such as the requirements of OSPAR within a European context.

Similarly, it was noted that a number of common and basic "principles" for protecting the environment – precautionary, polluter-pays, and so on – were now well established and that these also provided a basis for considering protection of the environment with respect to radiation. It was also felt desirable to ensure that any new approach taken was compatible with those already used for protection of the environment from the releases of metals and other chemicals. Indeed, many considered that such problems were of much greater urgency and therefore importance than any arising from the release of radionuclides; but these other problems had also received much greater attention in the past than had been given to the possible effects of radionuclides.

Considerable concern was expressed about the risk of any new initiatives to protect the environment undermining the system that already exists to protect people. And because people are an integral part of the environment it was considered, by some, that the current focus on protecting humans in an environmental context was correct. Nevertheless, it was recognised that protection of the environment – and how it could be explicitly demonstrated and delivered – was an ethical, social, and thus ultimately a political issue, and this applied as much to the nuclear industry as to any other. The manner in which it was to be resolved, and the demonstration of what a minor environmental problem it probably was, had therefore also to be addressed within this socio-political context.

Some thought that it was important to involve "stakeholders" in any new rationale or process. This would help to define the issues in the minds of the industry, its regulators, and the public, and thus also help to resolve them quickly. In this respect, the need for a greater dialogue between the industry and its regulators and advisors was essential, and thus the current ICRP-NEA initiative was very much welcomed and appreciated.

---

*   Kindly provided by Jan Pentreath.

SESSION 2

Scientific Knowledge and Ongoing Research-status, Objectives and Goals

Chair: Peter Burns, Australian Radiation Protection and Nuclear Safety Agency, Australia

A.   Taking Stock of International, Regional and National Developments

OUTCOMES OF THE IAEA PROGRAMME ON THE RADIOLOGICAL PROTECTION OF THE ENVIRONMENT

Carol Robinson
Division of Radiation and Waste Safety
International Atomic Energy Agency, Vienna

Abstract

Since the late 1990s the work of the International Atomic Energy Agency (IAEA), relating to the effects of radiation on species other than man, has been focused on defining and clarifying issues related to the development of an international framework to address the protection of the environment, or living elements within it, from the effects of ionising radiation.

In 1999, IAEA-TECDOC-1091, entitled *Protection of the Environment from the Effects of Ionising Radiation: A Report for Discussion*, was published. This report explored the various issues and approaches that would need to be resolved in order to establish an environmental protection framework and associated criteria. Relevant principles, policies and regulatory approaches were reviewed and the factors that may affect future developments of a protection system were identified. The report concluded that, although improved information was required in several areas, there was sufficient knowledge of the effects of ionising radiation on organisms to move forward.

Following publication of this report, IAEA activities have continued on: a) the elaboration of the ethics and principles underlying environmental protection, paying particular attention to their implications for the development of an approach for radiological protection of the environment; and, b) fostering information exchange by holding a series of Specialists Meetings on environmental radiation protection, the most recent of which took place in November 2001. The long-term aim of this work is to establish consensual IAEA Safety Standards on environmental radiation protection, in collaboration with other relevant international organisations.

This paper will provide a summary of IAEA work to date on the development of a framework for protection of the environment from ionising radiation, paying particular attention to the recently published IAEA-TECDOC-1270 on *Ethical Considerations in protecting the Environment from the Effects of Ionising Radiation*. This report explores the implication of ethical diversity on the development of internationally relevant protection principles, and identifies a number of principles implicit in international legal instruments. Categories of biological effects that may be used to assess "impact" or "harm" on living elements of the environment are discussed, together with proposals for future work needed to develop a practical environmental protection framework, including the detailed definition of targets, endpoints and appropriate criteria. This paper will also provide an overview of the conclusions of the IAEA Specialists Meetings on this subject.

Introduction

The International Atomic Energy Agency (IAEA) has a long history of involvement in the assessment of doses and risks to species other than man, as described in a related paper, also published in these proceedings. Following the Rio Declaration of 1992,[1] and the growing awareness of environmental issues, evidenced by this and other international commitments, the focus for IAEA work has been to explore issues related to the development of a system or framework for protection of the environment from the effects of ionising radiation. IAEA-TECDOC-1091 was published in 1999,[2] with the aim of identifying the main issues that would need to be resolved in developing a protection system, to form the basis of international discussions. These discussions have since been facilitated by holding a series of IAEA Specialists Meetings that also provided the opportunity for information exchange and discussion of work in progress elsewhere.

In addition to its actions to facilitate information exchange, the IAEA has continued its development work by considering the ethics and principles of environmental protection. It is clear that there are scientific, ethical and legal aspects that influence the way in which protection approaches and systems are developed and applied. These aspects are interlinked, but this categorisation is useful in unravelling the many different elements of relevance. The results of this process, undertaken as part of the Agency's work programme, can be found in the recently published IAEA-TECDOC-1270, on *Ethical Considerations in Protecting the Environment from the Effects of Ionising Radiation.*[3] A number of issues from this report are highlighted here for ease of reference.

Scientific background

The interactions between individual members of different species in the environment are complex, chaotic, and necessarily competitive. Any living organism is constantly under stress from other organisms and from abiotic agents. The relative numbers of individuals and species fluctuate in time and, over long periods of time, vary as a result of evolutionary changes. Human development increasingly perturbs these interactions.

It is known that detrimental effects on biota can be observed at radiation doses and dose rates considerably above those that occur naturally. Indeed, much of the current basic knowledge about the molecular and cellular mechanisms of radiation damage has come from studies with both animals and plants. Some detrimental effects (termed deterministic effects) manifest in individuals when the radiation dose absorbed by the organism exceeds some threshold – cell killing and resultant tissue damage, for example. Other detrimental effects (termed stochastic effects) manifest by an increase in the frequency of their occurrence, in a population, with increasing dose. Examples of such effects are the development of cancer in some animals, or mutation in the genome. A consequence of both deterministic and stochastic effects is that the lifespan of some organisms will be shortened, reproductive ability may be reduced, and the genome may be adversely affected. Were sufficient numbers of organisms in a given species to be affected in these ways, changes in populations could manifest, and any given ecosystem perturbed.

---

1. United Nations, Rio Declaration on Environment and Development (1992).

2. International Atomic Energy Agency, Protection of the Environment from the Effects of Ionizing Radiation, IAEA-TECDOC-1091, IAEA, Vienna (1999).

3. International Atomic Energy Agency, Ethical Considerations in Protecting the Environment from the Effects of Ionizing Radiation, IAEA-TECDOC-1270, IAEA, Vienna (2002).

Reviews of environmental radiation levels and radionuclide concentrations, and of the effects of radiation on biota, exist, notably by the United Nations Scientific Committee on the Effects of Atomic Radiation.[4,5] However, uncertainty remains about the actual radiation doses experienced by natural biota throughout their lifetimes, due partly to insufficiencies in the present dosimetric methods for biota. There is also no coherent model for predicting the likelihood of deterministic and stochastic effects that can be applied in a generic way for individual members of species, for populations, or whole ecosystems. The current situation is that assessments of the significance for health, competitive capabilities, and reproductive success of biota, resulting from anthropogenic additions to their radiation exposure, rely on compendia of empirical data on the relationships between deterministic or stochastic effects and radiation doses. There would be value in developing a more systematic and internationally agreed procedure.

Ethical aspects

Culture affects how scientific findings are interpreted and how ideas are developed. Cultures are influenced by religious traditions – or the lack of them – ideologies, politics, scientific understanding, education and world views. Different views of nature held by different cultures therefore affect their understanding of biological processes, including interpretations of radiation effects upon them, and their moral and ethical significance. Science, in turn, affects the way in which nature is viewed, and the rapid developments in the fields of biology and genetics are particularly relevant in this respect.

Environmental ethics has developed largely from existing human-based theories and concern with the philosophical question of moral standing. The most fundamental divergence is between anthropocentrism and non-anthropocentrism. Proponents of anthropocentrism regard human beings, their life and experiences as the only or main thing of moral standing. In this case, environmental protection is considered to be important only in so far as it affects humans.[6,7] Advocates of non-anthropocentrism reject the assertion that moral value can be derived and justified only in terms of human interests, and offer a variety of alternative ethical outlooks. Two representative non-anthropocentric outlooks are discussed[8] – biocentrism and ecocentrism.[9]

Biocentrism (literally "life-centred") has been broadly defined as an ethical outlook in which it is asserted that moral standing can be derived from a particular biological characteristic of individual members of a species. A necessary consequence of all biocentric outlooks is a recognition that individual life forms other than humans can have value in themselves, and should be respected for

4. United Nations, Sources and Effects of Ionizing Radiation (Report to the General Assembly) Scientific Committee on the Effects of Atomic Radiation (UNSCEAR), UN, New York (2000).

5. United Nations, Sources and Effects of Ionizing Radiation (Report to the General Assembly) Scientific Committee on the Effects of Atomic Radiation (UNSCEAR), UN, New York (1996).

6. Norton, B., Why Preserve Natural Variety? Princeton University Press: Princeton (1988).

7. Bookchin, M., The Ecology of Freedom, 2nd Edition, Black Rose Books: Montreal (1991).

8. International Atomic Energy Agency, Ethical Considerations in Protecting the Environment from the Effects of Ionizing Radiation, IAEA-TECDOC-1270, IAEA, Vienna (2002).

9. Callicott, J.B., Elements of an environmental ethic: moral considerability and the biotic community, Environmental Ethics, 1 (1979) 71–81.

what they are. Since biocentrism is focused on individuals rather than the diversity of species, these outlooks have also been described as an "individualistic" environmental ethic.[10,11,12]

Proponents of ecocentrism reject the assumption that morally-relevant value can be derived only from some biological attribute of individual organisms. Ecocentrists affirm that diversity of species, ecosystems, rivers, mountains and landscapes can have value in themselves, even if they do not affect the welfare of humans or other individual members of non-human species.[13,14,15] All ecocentrists attach particular value to the diversity, dynamics and interactions within a healthy ecosystem, but differ in their views on the cause of and solutions to modern environmental problems. The general concern for the biotic and abiotic community as a whole,[16] leads to the alternative classification of the ecocentric outlook as an "holistic" environmental ethic.[17,18]

There is now a greater concern for other forms of life, for nature and the environment in general, evidenced by a number of recent international legal instruments, of which the Rio Declaration on Environment and Development of 1992[19] is the most obvious. Thus, while there exists a diversity of ethical outlooks, international agreement has been reached on a number of "norms" that relate to the environment and its protection. A number of such "norms" were identified which would be of relevance in developing consistent principles for the protection of the environment from ionising radiation, as discussed below.

Legal aspects

Much of the early concern with respect to the natural world was centred around the loss of individual species or of unique natural areas. A greater understanding of the highly complex interdependence of wildlife, which cannot be sustained simply by conserving individual species, has also led to the consideration of the total variety of life on the planet, or biodiversity. There are three

10. Callicott, J.B., Elements of an environmental ethic: moral considerability and the biotic community, Environmental Ethics, 1 (1979) 71–81.

11. Rolston, H., III, Challenges in environmental ethics. Ecology, Economics, Ethics: The Broken Circle, Yale University Press: London (1991).

12. Sagoff, M., Animal liberation and environmental ethics: bad marriage quick divorce, Osgood Hall Law Journal, 22 (1984) 297–307.

13. Callicott, J.B., Elements of an environmental ethic: moral considerability and the biotic community, Environmental Ethics, 1 (1979) 71–81.

14. Næss, A., Økologi, Sammfunn og Livstil: Utkast til en Økosofi, Universitetsforlaget: Oslo. (Ecology, Community and Lifestyle: Outline of an Ecosophy, trans. D. Rothenburg, 1990, Cambridge University Press: Cambridge) (1974).

15. Callicott, J.B., In Defense of the Land Ethic. State University Press of New York: Albany (1989).

16. Leopold, A., A Sand County Almanac. 1949 (2nd Ed 1977). Oxford University Press. See also Callicott, J.B (Ed.), A Companion to A Sand County Almanac, University of Wisconsin: Madison (1987).

17. Callicott, J.B., Elements of an environmental ethic: moral considerability and the biotic community, Environmental Ethics, 1 (1979) 71–81.

18. Sagoff, M., Animal liberation and environmental ethics: bad marriage quick divorce, Osgood Hall Law Journal, 22 (1984) 297–307.

19. United Nations, Charter of the United Nations, San Francisco (1945).

elements to biodiversity: the diversity of habitats (or of ecological complexes); the diversity of species; and the diversity of the genetic variability within each species.

The Rio Declaration on Environment and Development in 1992,[20] was related to the maintenance of biodiversity, and to an additional environmental "norm" – sustainable development. This states that environmental protection constitutes an integral part of the sustainable development process; and commits States to "cooperate to…conserve, protect and restore the health and integrity of earth's ecosystem". Sustainable development thus implicitly includes the concept of maintenance of biodiversity. However, it also places focus on inter-generational equity.

Human rights issues are also of relevance to this discussion. There will be times when some human interests will be in opposition to the other human interests and to the need to protect other species. The need to make decisions in the light of such opposing interests brings other international "norms" into play – those related to justice and human rights.

Legal instruments exist that relate to liability and compensation for environmental damage or stress. This issue is also included in the principles of the 1992 Rio Declaration.[21] The concept of "environmental justice" underlying these issues is discussed in more detail in IAEA-TECDOC-1270.[22] Human rights are a cornerstone of the Charter of the United Nations,[23] and the need to take different views and interests into account when making decisions is discussed in Reference 3 under a general heading of "human dignity".

Application of protection principles

In assessing the impact of ionising radiation on biota, three "norms" or principles have been defined[24] that can be applied directly: conservation, maintenance of biodiversity, and sustainability. The first two follow directly from the discussion above. The issue of "sustainability" is a little different – it does not involve "development" aspects, but the concept of ensuring inter-generational equity is retained. These principles can be used in combination with scientific information, relating to deleterious biological effects of ionising radiation and the scale of such effects (exposure or dose), as part of an assessment framework to evaluate the possible impact of radiation on the environment or biota within it.

The principle of sustainability implies that impacts on future generations and productivity are of particular concern and that the quality of the environment should not be diminished over time. Maintaining biodiversity and conservation (or habitat protection) are important considerations in their own right, but they are also essential features of the application of the principle of sustainability. Under normal circumstances, the primary impact of ionising radiation is on living tissue. Thus, the main focus for protection of the environment from the effects of ionising radiation is likely to be on the protection of biota from radiation-induced early mortality, increased morbidity, reduced

20. United Nations, Rio Declaration on Environment and Development (1992).

21. United Nations, Rio Declaration on Environment and Development (1992).

22. International Atomic Energy Agency, Ethical Considerations in Protecting the Environment from the Effects of Ionizing Radiation, IAEA-TECDOC-1270, IAEA, Vienna (2002).

23. United Nations, Charter of the United Nations, San Francisco (1945).

24. International Atomic Energy Agency, Ethical Considerations in Protecting the Environment from the Effects of Ionizing Radiation, IAEA-TECDOC-1270, IAEA, Vienna (2002).

reproductive success and deleterious hereditary effects. Occurrence of each of these would influence sustainability, maintenance of biodiversity and conservation.

In making environmental management decisions, there is a need to balance the interests of protecting biota relative to human. The two other principles – those related to human dignity and to environmental justice – inform these judgements.

The principle of human dignity can inform judgements made between the interests of humans and biota, providing some support for preference to be given to human interests relative to those of biota. The same principle can help to resolve issues that arise with different human interests, and support the idea that those affected should be involved in making the decision (informed consent).

The principle of environmental justice implies, for example, that those humans who do not receive benefits from a practice should not have their interests affected by environmental harm arising from it and, if they do, that some compensation may be appropriate.

Conclusions

The development of legal instruments and protection frameworks are strongly influenced by the cultural background of the people developing and adopting them. This cultural background has religious, non-religious, ethical and scientific elements that can vary greatly amongst IAEA Member States. In developing an international framework for protection of the environment from the effects of ionising radiation, it is therefore necessary to recognise and take account of these different viewpoints and IAEA-TECDOC-1270[25] represents a step in this process.

There is a consensus emerging that the principles discussed above provide a reasonable basis for the development of a framework for environmental protection.[26,27] Under normal circumstances, the main direct impact of ionising radiation on environmental media relates to its inter-action with living tissue. Thus, the assessment of effects on biota is likely to be the primary focus of a framework for protection of the environment from ionising radiation. In order to develop a practical framework for assessing the impact of ionising radiation on biota, it is necessary to link the five principles with scientific information relating to radiation-induced changes. Four types of effect have been considered to be relevant (morbidity, early mortality, reduced reproductive success and deleterious hereditary effects).[28,29,30]

25. International Atomic Energy Agency, Ethical Considerations in Protecting the Environment from the Effects of Ionizing Radiation, IAEA-TECDOC-1270, IAEA, Vienna (2002).

26. Statement from the Consensus Conference on the Protection of the Environment, part of the seminar "Radiation Protection in the 21st Century: Ethical, Philosophical and Environment Issues", Norwegian Academy of Science and Letters. Oslo, 22–25 October 2001, http://www.iur-uir.org.

27. International Atomic Energy Agency, Summary Report of the Specialists Meeting on Environmental Protection from the Effects of Ionising Radiation: International Perspectives, SP-1114.3, 26–29 November 2001, IAEA, Vienna (2001).

28. International Atomic Energy Agency, Ethical Considerations in Protecting the Environment from the Effects of Ionizing Radiation, IAEA-TECDOC-1270, IAEA, Vienna (2002).

29. Pentreath, R.J., A System for Radiological Protection of the Environment: Some initial Thoughts and Ideas, Journal of Radiological Protection, 19 (1999) 117–128.

30. Pentreath, R.J., Radiation Protection of Man and the Environment: Developing a Common Approach, Journal of Radiological Protection, 22 (2002) 45–56.

The challenge now is to build on this ethical base and set of protection principles, the scientific and management framework that will guide Member States in implementing programmes to assure adequate protection of biota. The activities needed to meet this challenge are to:

- Define the options for measurements and estimation in safety assessments.

- Consolidate and interpret the existing relevant data on the effects of ionising radiation on biota in the natural state and on the behaviour of radionuclides in the biotic and abiotic parts of the environment.

- Identify where the most significant gaps are in the data base and undertake research programmes to obtain the needed data.

- Develop the management options for making decisions that will be adaptable to the variety of situations in all Member States.

Progress is being made in all these areas by the IAEA, and a variety of other organisations, as discussed in more detail elsewhere.[31,32]

Acknowledgements

The author would like to acknowledge the contribution of the following experts in the development of IAEA-TECDOC-1270, and consequently the ideas presented in this paper: Mary Clark, Environmental Protection Agency, USA, Carl Reinhold Bråkenhielm, University of Uppsala, Sweden, David Kocher, Oak Ridge National Laboratory, USA, Carl-Magnus Larsson, Swedish Radiation Protection Authority, Sweden, Richard Osborne, Ranasara Consultants Inc., Canada, Deborah Oughton, International Union of Radioecology and Jan Pentreath, University of Reading, UK.

31. International Atomic Energy Agency, Ethical Considerations in Protecting the Environment from the Effects of Ionizing Radiation, IAEA-TECDOC-1270, IAEA, Vienna (2002).

32. Canadian Nuclear Safety Commission, Environmental Protection Approaches for Nuclear Facilities, Proceedings of the Second International Symposium on Ionizing Radiation, Ottawa 1999, May 10–14, CNSC, Ottawa (2001).

International Union of Radioecology, Doses and Effects in Non-Human Systems, Work of the IUR Environmental Transfer Action Group 1997–1999, IUR, Østeras, Norway (2000).

United States Department of Energy, Graded Approach for Evaluating Radiation Doses to Aquatic and Terrestrial Biota, US DOE Draft Standard (1999).

Copplestone, D., et al., Impact Assessment of Ionising Radiation on Wildlife, R&D Publication 128, Environment Agency, Bristol, UK (2001).

Strand, P., LARSSON, C-M., Delivering a Framework for the Protection of the Environment from Ionizing Radiation, in Radioactive Pollutants, Impact on the Environment, Eds. Bréchignac, F., and Howard, B.J., EDP Sciences, les Veix, France (2001).

FRAMEWORK FOR ASSESSMENT OF ENVIRONMENTAL IMPACT (FASSET)

C. Magnus Larsson
Head, Department of Waste Management and Environmental Protection
Swedish Radiation Protection Authority

Abstract

The overall aim of the FASSET project is to develop a framework within which assessment models, relevant to the impact of ionising radiation on the environment, can be applied and results analysed for European ecosystems. Complete documentation on the FASSET project can be found on the FASSET's web-site (www.fasset.org). This paper describes the current state of the project, based on the project's first Annual Report.

Seven European ecosystems are considered; four terrestrial (natural forests, semi-natural pastures, agricultural ecosystems and wetlands) and three aquatic (marine, brackish and freshwater). In FASSET Deliverable 1 a list of candidate generic *reference organisms* has been drawn up on the basis of expert judgement of exposure situations in the selected ecosystems. They serve as a starting points for development of dosimetric models, and for pooling available information on ecological relevance and biological effects. Further analysis of the candidate reference organisms is performed to justify their choice and assess their applicability in different situations, taking into account modelling of radionuclide transfer, estimates of internal and external dose rates, ecological significance and biological effects.

Four general "umbrella" radiation effects on biota are considered that, when manifested in an individual, may have an impact at population level or at higher levels of the organisational hierarchy. The four "umbrellas" are: morbidity (fitness or well-being), mortality (death directly attributable to radiation), reproductive success (changed number of offspring) and scorable cytogenetic effects (molecular actions, aberrations). A database is being assembled, compiling dose and dose rates data from the literature for a number of organism categories for each of these four umbrella effects. The database also considers the suitability of data to derive the relative biological efficiency (RBE) for different types of radiation.

The work from the three work packages on exposure, dosimetry and effects will be organised into a framework for impact assessments, which will take into account experiences from application of ecotoxicological approaches in assessing effects of other hazardous substances. Characterisation of risks will be performed in a way that attempts to make the framework useful to regulators, for demonstration of compliance, and for communicating with the public and decision-makers.

1.   Objectives of the FASSET project

The requirement for assessments of the environmental effects of radiation is increasing due to growing public concern for environmental protection issues and integration of environmental impact assessments into the regulatory process. Thus, there is a strong need to establish a framework for the assessment of environmental impact of ionising radiation, as well as a system for protection of the environment from ionising radiation. The FASSET project aims at providing a formalistic framework for assessment of radiation effects on biota and ecosystems. The project has the following practical objectives:

- To provide a set of reference organisms relevant to different exposure situations. The identification of reference organisms must take into account the environmental fate of radionuclide releases, exposure pathways, dosimetry and biological effects.

- To provide a set of models for the reference organisms, including models for environmental transport of radionuclides, exposure, dosimetry and biological effects.

- To critically examine reported data on biological effects on individual, population and ecosystem levels, as a point of departure for characterising the environmental consequences of, e.g., a source releasing radioactive substances into the environment.

- To review existing frameworks for environmental assessment used in different environmental management or protection programmes. This review will extend outside the field of radiation protection, and consider, *inter alia*, frameworks for managing risks from genotoxic chemicals. The resulting FASSET framework will thus be set in a wider context of assessments of environmental effects and management of risks to the environment.

2.   Project status

The project status after one year is described in the Annual Report, found on the FASSET website, www.fasset.org. The following description is a brief summary of the first year's achievements, which also illustrates the project's general direction.

2.1   *The reference organism concept*

A special feature within FASSET is the focus on *reference organisms*. This approach is analogous to the *reference man* concept that has been adopted within radiological protection to provide a standard set of models and datasets. The project's working definition of the reference organism is:

"a series of imaginary entities that provide a basis for the estimation of radiation dose rate to a range of organisms which are typical, or representative, of a contaminated environment. These estimates, in turn, would provide a basis for assessing the likelihood and degree of radiation effects. It is important that they are not a direct representation of any identifiable animal or plant species".

An initial step in the construction of the framework is thus the selection of appropriate reference organisms. The final choice of reference organisms for consideration within the FASSET framework will be an iterative process taking into account dosimetry as well as radioecological criteria and radiosensitivity. The interaction between the different sub-projects (work packages) on dosimetry, exposure, biological effects and framework, respectively, in the selection of reference organisms is shown schematically in Figure 1.

2.2   *Dosimetric considerations*

Monte Carlo calculations for external irradiation have been performed for various reference organisms. The calculations were made for monoenergetic gamma energies of 50 keV, 300 keV, 662 keV, 1 MeV and 3 MeV. The source of the emitters was assumed to be planar on the soil or in depths of 5 and 20 cm.

Figure 1. **The interaction between FASSET work packages (WP) needed for the selection of reference organisms**

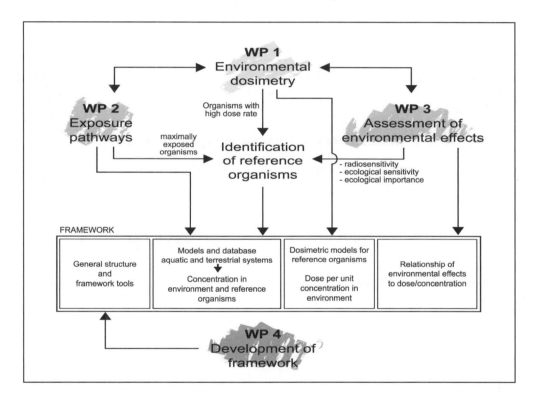

With regard to external radiation, the exposure of aquatic organisms from natural radionuclides has been discussed. The radionuclides were U-238, Th-232, Th-230, Ra-228, Ra-226, Rn-222, Po-210 and K-40. The doses were calculated for a variety of organisms such as bacteria, phyto- and zooplankton, crustaceans, fish. The highest weighted doses were found for benthic molluscs and large benthic crustaceans for typical concentrations in water in the order of 6 µGy/h. For the case of high U-concentrations in water the dose rates were about 10 times higher. In both instances, Po-210 was by far the most important contributor to the dose rate. The most sensitive parameters were the concentration factors and the RBE weighting factor for alpha radiation

The work to be done for the estimation of exposures due to internal emitters has been defined. It has been agreed that it is not possible and not necessary to consider a large number of organisms, but to define a set of organism sizes and energies, that allows the assessment of exposures to a wide range of possible species. The most important quantity to assess internal exposures is the fraction of energy absorbed in the organism, which depends on the radiation type, the energy and the size and geometry of the reference organism. In a first step, it has been agreed to assume a homogeneous distribution in the reference organisms.

Table 1. Energy and geometry specifications for calculations of internal exposures in animals

Radiation type	Energy range	Size range	Geometry
γ	20 keV–3 MeV	0.01–1 m	Ellipsoids
β	5 keV–4 MeV	10^{-5}–0.03 m	Ellipsoids
α	3–10 MeV	10^{-5}–10^{-3} m	Spheres

For herbaceous vegetation, a shrub and a tree were selected as possible reference organisms to represent the flora. Agreement was found that these plants could be represented appropriately by the following specifications:

Table 2. Geometries for calculation of exposures in plants

Plant type	Height	Target organ	Height of plant part considered
Herb	0–0.1 m	Meristem	at the ground (0 m)
Shrub	0.1–1 m	Bud, meristem	in middle of canopy (0.55 m)
Tree	1–10 m	Bud, meristem	in middle of canopy (5.5 m)

Meristems have been defined as target organs, since these are assumed to be most sensitive to irradiation due to the intensive cell division.

2.3   *Exposure in different ecosystems*

The initial work on exposure in different ecosystems was concerned with the identification of candidate reference organisms from the point of view of *radioecological sensitivity*. The factors determining radioecological sensitivity are:

- whether the habitat or feeding habits of the organism are likely to maximise its potential exposure to radionuclides, based on an understanding of the distribution of the different radionuclides within the ecosystem;

- whether the organism exhibits radionuclide-specific bioconcentration,[1] which is likely to maximise internal radionuclide exposures in particular circumstances;

---

1. Here, bioconcentration is used to refer to a situation where an organism accumulates internally (inside the organism's body) a radionuclide to concentrations higher than those that exist in the surrounding media, e.g. water column (dissolved phase), sediment or soil.

- whether the position of the organism within the foodchain (e.g. top predator) is such that biomagnification[2] of radionuclides up the foodchain may lead to enhanced accumulation.

In order to identify the candidate reference organisms, major European ecosystems have been characterised in terms of their ecological characteristics, important pathways and radionuclide transfer. Based upon our knowledge of the distribution of radionuclides within the environment, a simplified compartmentalisation has been used: soil, herbaceous layer and canopy for terrestrial ecosystems; bed sediment and water column for aquatic ecosystems. Some organisms may be present in different compartments, most notably the roots and above ground parts of plants. The project considered simplified ecological niches/organism groupings within the selection process, to ensure that candidate reference organisms will be sufficient to protect the environment as a whole within any assessment. In this selection the availability of data for an organism, or the ability in the future to obtain the required data are also considered.

The approach taken towards the selection of these should ensure that suitable reference organisms are available for a range of scenarios (chronic and acute exposure) and different European ecosystems. In total 31 candidate reference organisms have been suggested representing marine, freshwater and a variety of terrestrial ecosystems. The complete list (Table 3) and the reasoning behind the selection is found in Deliverable 1 (Strand *et al.*, 2001), also available on www.fasset.org.

Table 3. **Candidate reference organisms for terrestrial and aquatic ecosystems**

Terrestrial ecosystems	Aquatic ecosystems
Soil	**Sediment**
Soil micro-organisms	Benthic bacteria
Soil invertebrates, "worms"	Benthic invertebrates, "worm"
Plants and fungi	Molluscs
Burrowing mammals	Crustaceans
	Vascular plants
Herbaceous layer	Amphibians
Bryophytes	Fish
Grasses, herbs and crops	Fish eggs
Shrubs	Wading birds
Above ground invertebrates	Sea mammals
Herbivorous mammals	
Carnivorous mammals	**Water column**
Reptiles	Phytoplankton
Vertebrate eggs	Zooplankton
Amphibians	Macroalgae
Birds	Fish
	Sea mammals
Canopy	
Trees	
Invertebrates	

---

2. Similarly, biomagnification is used to refer to a situation where concentrations of radionuclides in organisms increase as one moves higher up the foodchain.

2.4   *Biological effects of ionising radiation*

Effects and umbrella effects

There are a large number of effects that have been used to describe radiation impact and construct dose-response relationships. Many of the earlier studies have been on the determination of LD 50 values for comparative radiosensitivity purposes, i.e. acute radiation exposures (usually in < 10 seconds or minutes) were employed to determine the resulting short term mortality (usually within 30 days). Experimental studies on the effects of low dose rate, chronic radiation exposure, have provided data not only on mortality (frequently, a relatively minor effect), but also on fertility, fecundity (or their combination as total reproductive performance), growth rate, somatic and germ cell mutation rates, and so on. Because all the effects that have been observed at the individual level could be presumed to have some possible consequence at the population level, it was decided that FASSET would concentrate on **four umbrella effects** that have significance at the population level:

- morbidity (including growth rate, effects on the immune system, and the behavioural consequences of damage to the central nervous system from radiation exposure in the developing embryo);

- mortality (including stochastic effect of somatic mutation and its possible consequence of cancer induction, as well as deterministic effects in particular tissues or organs that would change the age-dependent death rate);

- reduced reproductive success (including fertility – the production of functional gametes, and fecundity – the survival of the embryo through development to an entity separate from its parents);

- cytogenetic effects (i.e. indicator of mutation induction in germ and somatic cells).

It is recognised that these four categories of effect are not mutually exclusive – e.g. effects leading to changes in morbidity may result in a change in the age-dependent death rate, and an increase in mutation rate may lead to changes in reproductive success. They simply provide a convenient means of summarising the available information in a structured way that is meaningful within the objectives of the FASSET project.

In part, the four "umbrella" effects cover the range of relative radiosensitivities within an organism and suggest targets that might be of significance for the purpose of dosimetry:

- the whole body if there is no information on the differential distribution of radionuclides within the organism (this would be relevant for mortality – including stochastic mutation rates in somatic tissues – and morbidity);

- the gonads (fertility and heritable mutations) and the meristems in plants (both for mortality – damage to growth potential – and the gamete bearing tissues);

- externally developing embryos and seeds;

- specific tissues or organs if data are available.

In order to organise the available information on biological effects in a useful way for the framework, a database is being built, aimed at relating dose or dose rates to effects for the specific purpose of FASSET. The collection of data for the database is currently ongoing.

2.5   Framework

The general structure of existing frameworks for environmental risk assessment has been considered to be appropriate also for FASSET; i.e. a division of the assessment into three stages; problem formulation, risk assessment and risk management, see Figure 2.

The risk management stage lies outside the scope of the FASSET project. The emphasis of FASSET is the development of tools and data for the risk assessment phase of this ecological risk assessment and management process. However, the construction of the FASSET framework must be flexible in order to take into account the various risk management options, as well as societal concern defined in the formulation stage, as these influence (and ultimately must make use of) the way in which a risk assessment is carried out.

Figure 2. **Schematic representation of a generic framework**

Ecological risk assessment and management		
Problem formulation	**Risk assessment**	**Risk management**
Description and definiton of assessment context	**Methodologies and results relevant to**	**Prevention, mitigation and elimination of consequences**
• Purpose	• Exposure analysis	
• Philosophy	• Effects analysis	
• Source characterisation and hazard identification	• Risk characterisation and consequence analysis	
• Spatial and temporal conside-rations		
• Identification of the object of protection		
• Identification of what is to be measured/predicted in order to determine the degree of protection		
• Treatment of background		

The way in which problem formulation is carried out in the different assessment systems studied differ, depending mainly on the different aims and philosophies of the assessments. The FASSET framework must be appropriate for varying formulated problems, e.g. FASSET must:

- be able to take into account ongoing, past and future releases;

- be able to take into account chronic and acute effects:

- be appropriate for assessments carried out for various purposes, e.g. licensing, demonstration of compliance, assessment of accidents, decisions concerning remediation.

Some of the elements of other frameworks will be included and appropriately adapted within FASSET, together with a justification for the approach taken. This information will be presented in Deliverable 2, due by the end of 2002.

3. Following FASSET progress

3.1 *Deliverables*

The project has so far delivered one, out of six (see FASSET Technical Annex on www.fasset.org), reports or deliverables scheduled in the project plan. Deliverable 1 (2001) consists of one main report and two appendices, and are available on the website:

- Report: Identification of candidate reference organisms from a radiation exposure pathways perspective (Eds: Strand, Beresford, Avila, Jones and Larsson. Contributors: Agüero, Barnett, Brown, Gilek, Howard, Ilus, Kautsky, Kumblad, Näslund, Patton, Robles, Sanchez, Saxén, Stensrud, Suañez, Wright).

- Appendix 1. Ecological characteristics of European terrestrial ecosystems: Overview of radiation exposure pathways relevant to the identification of candidate reference organisms.

- Appendix 2. Ecological characteristics of European aquatic ecosystems: Overview of radiation exposure pathways relevant to the identification of candidate reference organisms.

3.2 *Communicating FASSET to wider audiences*

The Consortium acknowledged at an early stage the need for the project to be open and transparent, and allow anyone interested to follow its development. A web-site, www.fasset.org, was therefore created, and an information leaflet produced to inform of the project and to promote its web-site.

The web-site is divided into a public domain and members' area (password-protected). The organisation of the public domain of the web-site and its material is as follows:

- FASSET leaflet.

- Final version of deliverables.

- List of publications supported by FASSET project.

- Progress reports/Mid term reports.

- Technical annex.

- Databases (e.g. on radiation effects).[3]

In order to respond to the interest shown by "external" stakeholders, and to gain important information, the Consortium organised an External Forum to take place in Bath, UK, 8-9 April 2002. Invitations have been sent to 22 international and national organisations representing industry, regulators, and environmental groups.

3.3   FASSET/BIOMASS workshop

The International Atomic Energy Agency (IAEA) is concluding its project on Biosphere Modelling and Assessment (BIOMASS). The project has clear relevance to FASSET as regards to for example problem formulation, but also other aspects resulting from the problem formulation, such as the selection of biosphere system.

A workshop was held, 30–31 October in Stockholm, to identify which BIOMASS issues are relevant to FASSET, and how FASSET can continue developing concepts within the BIOMASS methodology. The workshop was attended by eight FASSET partners and by IAEA, and also by ANDRA (France) to exchange information between FASSET and the on-going 5th Framework Programme Project BIOCLIM (Modelling Sequential Biosphere Systems under Climate Change for Radioactive Waste Disposal).

3.4   Publications and presentations

Publications

Avila, R. & Larsson, C.M. (2001) A probabilistic approach to radiological environmental impact assessment. *Proceeding of VALDOR 2001 (Values in Decisions on Risk)*, Stockholm, Sweden, 10-14 June 2001.

Pentreath, R.J. & Woodhead, D.S. (2001) A system for protecting the environment from ionising radiation: selecting reference fauna and flora, and the possible dose models and environmental geometries that could be applied to them. *Sci. Total Env. 277*, pages 33-43.

Strand, P. & Larsson, C.M. (2001) Delivering a framework for the protection of the environment from ionising radiation. In *Radioactive Pollutants. Impact on the Environment (F. Brechignac and B.J. Howard, eds.)*. EDP Sciences, Les Ulis, France.

Strand *et al.,* (2001) Deliverable 1 (see 3.1. above).

---

3. Members area initially. Public area, when problems concerning database protection/input quality have been solved.

Pentreath, R.J. (2002) *Radiation protection of man and the environment: developing a common approach.* J. Radiol. Prot. (In press).

Symposia and other meetings

The FASSET project, and its results, has been/will be presented, discussed and publicised in a number of symposia and other meetings. Examples for 2001 and 2002 are:

- Joint Policy Debate on Protection of the Environment, organised by the Radioactive Waste Management Committee and the Committee for Radiation Protection and Public Health, of the OECD Nuclear Energy Agency, Paris, 7 March 2001.

- VALDOR 2001 (Values in Decisions on Risk), Stockholm, 10-14 June 2001.

- ECORAD (International Congress on the Radioecology-Ecotoxicology of Continental and Estuarine Environments), Aix-en-Provence, 3–7 September 2001.

- NKS/IUR Consensus Conference on Protection of the Environment, Radiation Protection in the 21st Century: Ethical, Philosophical and Environmental Issues, Oslo, 22-25 October 2001.

- IAEA, 2nd Specialists' Meeting on Protection of the Environment from the Effects of Ionizing Radiation, Vienna, 26-30 November 2001.

- IUR-SETAC, Joint International Seminar on Exposure and Effects, Modelling in Environmental Toxicology, Antwerp, 4-8 February 2002.

- OECD/NEA-ICRP seminar, Taormina, Sicily, February 2002.

- 5th International Conference on Environmental Radioactivity in the Arctic and Antarctic, St. Petersburg, Russia, 16-20 June 2002.

- 3rd International Symposium on the Protection of the Environment from Ionising Radiation, Darwin, Australia, 22-26 July 2002.

- International Conference on Radioactivity in the Environment, Monaco, 1-5 September 2002.

Website: *www.fasset.org*

Appendix

FASSET PARTNERS

Contractors:

Swedish Radiation Protection Authority	SSI
Swedish Nuclear Fuel and Waste Management Co.	SKB
Environment Agency of England and Wales	EA
German Federal Office for Radiation Protection	BfS
German National Centre for Environment and Health	GSF
Spanish Research Centre in Energy, Environment and Technology	CIEMAT
Radiation and Nuclear Safety Authority, Finland	STUK
Norwegian Radiation Protection Authority	NRPA

Assistant Contractors:

Kemakta Konsult AB, Sweden	Kemakta
Stockholm University, Sweden	SU
Centre for Ecology and Hydrology, UK	CEH
Westlakes Scientific Consulting Ltd, UK	WSC
Centre for Environment, Fisheries and Aquaculture Sciences, UK	CEFAS
University of Reading, UK	UR
Institut de Protection et de Sûreté Nucléaire, France	IPSN

B.   Specific Considerations

WHAT HARM DO WE WANT TO PROTECT AGAINST AND HOW SHOULD IT BE ASSESSED?

Norman Gentner
UNSCEAR

A coherent philosophical framework and set of ethical principles are required for guidance on how to protect the environment from the effects of ionising radiation. These are being provided by the ICRP and the IAEA. Of equal importance, however, are the "nuts-and-bolts" of selecting appropriate assessment and measurement endpoints, as these serve not only to determine whether adverse effects may exist but also to demonstrate compliance. This part of the environmental protection framework involves, in some form or another, the formulation of estimated exposure values (EEV's) and estimated-no-effects-values (ENEV's). The latter can take the form of either dose or (preferably) dose-rate criteria. Improved attention to and methods for dose estimation to lower-form biota are needed, as dosimetry impacts on both EEV and ENEV. More realistic models – taking into account radionuclide distribution, absorbed fraction and radiation weighting factors – are needed. Other important concerns for environmental assessments also need to be addressed at the "working level". We know how individual members of a species may be affected by radiation; we need to know how this type of information is related demonstrably to effects on populations or ecosystems. We know a lot about the effects of essentially acute exposure (though on a limited number of species); we need to know more about the effect of dose-rate protraction on assessment and measurement endpoints, and how best to convert what are essentially dose data to dose-rate criteria.

The UNSCEAR 1996 Report ("Effects of radiation on the environment") identified reproductive capacity as the most radiosensitive population attribute. The assessment by UNSCEAR provided dose-rate criteria: as an example, for natural plant and animal communities, a dose-rate of 0.1 mGy/h to a small proportion of individuals was deemed unlikely to have any detrimental effect at the population level. This and related dose-rate criteria remain defensible. In the programme of work begun 2001, UNSCEAR plans to develop a new scientific annex addressing radio ecology and effects of radiation on the environment. The scope includes: defining appropriate biotic endpoints for assessments; identifying the best methods to estimate doses to non-human biota, and performing real-life assessments of impacts at contaminated sites.

A special caution is urged if data on radiation-induced mutations *per se* are utilised as part of environmental assessments, as the average rate of radiation-induced mutation applicable in the context of environmental risk assessment is likely to be much lower than assumed from studies of induced mutation in non-essential genes, which is usually what is involved. Findings from the UNSCEAR 2001 Report ("Hereditary effects of radiation") illustrate this point.

WHAT DO WE CLEARLY KNOW ON ENVIRONMENTAL IMPACT AND ITS CAUSES?

Jean-Claude Barescut
IRSN, France

Impact or fluctuations?

A first question is to identify an environmental impact and a second one is to identify its causes. Responses to such questions are not straightforward since changes in the environment are quite usual. The desert borders are going forward and backward, as do forests, coral reefs or other important ecological systems. Climate may be the initial cause but there are also examples of cyclic evolution of animal populations that may be due to complex interactions between predators, prey and plant biomass resources. The difficulty inherent when identifying an impact is to be able to distinguish between fluctuations around a dynamic equilibrium and changes that have a persistent trend and that may eventually arise from human activity. Identifying an impact poses the same problem as identifying its causes. In any case, this requires sufficient ecological knowledge.

What measures, for what?

When facing the task of identifying an impact it is unwise to rely too much on measurements. This is an irrepressible temptation for radioactivity since it is easily measurable well below natural levels. It is certainly useful but only constitutes a first step in diagnostic. What we are interested in are sanitary consequences, decreases in populations, biodiversity or in biomass production. As a consequence, raw measurements of radioactivity are useful only if we can link them to such real effects.

Nevertheless, it is not realistic to expect too many monitoring data. Measurements are always partial, at least because of the delay and the distance between them. What is needed is a framework into which they can fit so as to support explanations, criticisms and interpolations. This leads to elaborating models, and of course to the need to validate them and hence suitable data to support validation.

Sometimes, simple monitoring data are sufficient to support the validation of some specific parts of models. For example, Chernobyl data were, and still are, largely used. But this proves not to be sufficient when attempting to validate complex phenomena. In such a case, a high sensitivity of measurements is required, and even, most importantly, full sets of simultaneous data that associate effects and suspected causes. Simple monitoring of radioactivity proves not to be sufficient, other parameters are also needed. Furthermore, in-situ data are not sufficient to validate models dealing with situations not yet encountered. Laboratory approaches are therefore necessary, not only to design experiments for easier use in validation, but also to address prognosis situations that are not observable.

Data are useless without a theoretical framework. One can do the most complicated and precise measurements, count atoms, count DNA mutations, this will be wasted if not supported by a sufficient effort to understand, and hence by research. Impact evaluation cannot rely only on radioactivity measurements.

Multiple stressors

There is no fundamental difference between radiotoxicity and other sources of toxicity. For risk assessment in simple cases the "ecotoxicological approach" may be used: finding the level at which a visible negative effect appears, and taking a safety margin from this level. In such cases, this method may either be applied to primary data such as concentration of toxicants, or to derived indicators such as the dose that is used in radioprotection. But the validity of this method is restricted to two conditions:

First, the toxicant should be largely dominant as compared to other stressors. If not, the effect/no-effect boundary has no chance of becoming clear-cut, but rather will be a complicated multidimensional surface that cannot be explored by a few measurements.

The second condition roots from the fact that to allow for an operational use of the tolerable concentration level, as measured in the environment, it is necessary to be able to evaluate the corresponding concentration level close to the target which may, or may not, be identical. Direct measurement is only possible in the case of an homogeneous environment since then, the sample may be taken anywhere. But this is not the usual case. Biological activity is often responsible for very strong concentration gradients. For example, the water composition may be fairly different if taken at the surface of a plant root, or far away from it. It may also be influenced by symbiotic associations: one partner being responsible for the conditions to which another partner is submitted.

In most usual situations of radioecological impact, the previous conditions are not fulfilled. There is a superimposition of combined effects due to others toxicants, to interactions with resources, or to indirect effects. For example a decrease of soil fertility may result from a primary effect on its microbial activity... Furthermore, there are predator-prey interactions. Even if the predator is not a direct victim, he will suffer in situations where the abundance of its prey is reduced.

Finally, there are also the very important effects linked to recycling and chemical speciation. After the first impact, the toxicant may be recycled many times. Its chemical form may change and hence, its bioavailability.

Symbiotic phenomena are the cause of important limitations inherent to simple toxicity tests. In a real ecosystem, each component is depending on the others for its nutrient supply and for the recycling of its wastes. The very process of life in the biosphere is self-supported by means of such symbiotic associations of several living components: there is no known example of a closed system with only one living component. In order to maintain life in a simple test system, nutrients have to be supplied and wastes cleaned. In these conditions, the lack of toxicity for a unique test organism does not provide the proof that another essential symbiotic organism, in a real situation, will not be affected by this toxicant. The most favourable situation is when a symbiotic organism eliminates the toxicant or reduces its bioavailability (for example, selenium excess in soil may be volatilised by microorganisms). But the worse case is when a key living component is suffering from the toxicant. This is the essential reason for the important, but blind, safety margins required when transposing from simple tests to real situations.

The conclusion is clear: any stress cannot be handled apart from others, nor independently from the ecological context.

IRSN research directions

The complexity of the problem does not necessarily mean that acceptable solutions will require a perfect understanding of life from the level of DNA all the way up to that of the biosphere. The generation of a large array of results useful for operational needs can be expected in a reasonable time and within a reasonable research investment. IRSN (Institute of Radioprotection and Nuclear Safety) in charge of the radiological monitoring of the environment in France, leads such research with a permanent concern for operational applications. Sub-set examples of such research are illustrated in the following.

Non-homogeneity

The problem

The first and main topic is environmental non-homogeneity. In current situations of radioactivity release in the environment, the total amount of radioactivity is small as compared to either the size of the biosphere and the size of the part of the geosphere in close interaction with it. Hence, added radioactivity becomes noticeable only if it is concentrated in some specific part of ecosystems, or if some processes cause a spontaneous concentration within sub-systems.

At the individual level, the dose concept is based on energy deposition. In the case of gamma radiation, either coming from outside or from an internal source, the energy is nearly evenly distributed inside the organs. This is why the energy, and the energy per unit of time, are good parameters that may be linked to real effects such as human cancers, as has been demonstrated with the Hiroshima situation.

In the case of alpha or beta radiations, the situation is more difficult since they deliver their energy within a very short distance range from their source. If the radionuclide source of the radiation is evenly distributed, as is the case for tritium or 14-carbon, the situation is very similar to the gamma radiation case and there is a good chance that "dose" may be trusted. But if the radionuclide has a specific affinity for some organs, or for some molecular constituents of the cells, it is clear that the energy distribution may be very non-homogeneous and that the dose concept turns out not to be very reliable. The question is not only academic. There are examples like the concentration of iodine in the thyroid after Chernobyl that may be responsible of non-negligible doses even far from the source. At this level, a factor 10 for the uncertainty on the dose, which is already a good performance for this kind of evaluation, may be crucial.

There are many data related to Cs and Sr. It is now well documented from Chernobyl that when these radionuclides are predominant, up to a dose rate of 1mGy/day, there is no obvious deleterious effect on biota. Even 10 mGy/day(over-passed only in some limited spots), involving some (limited) changes at the DNA level, do not appear to promote deleterious effects at the population level. Since these radionuclides are never far from homogeneous in organs, there is no reason to suspect important errors in dose evaluation. Unfortunately, this confidence level collapses in situations where the energy release is not evenly distributed. Furthermore, in situations where both the energy is unevenly distributed and the hottest spots coincide with the most sensitive target, the effect on biota could be more important than what could be expected from a dose calculation based on an hypothesis of homogeneity.

It is easy to imagine some scenarios where non-homogeneity could be a problem. It is the case for the 79-selenium distribution. During one century, the French production of 79-selenium will amount to 500 kg. This would be the stock in a typical waste repository. Due to its long life-time (1.1 My), it is difficult to exclude any Se escape from a repository. As a second bothering characteristic, Se is a very rare element that is also necessary for life. Its mean concentration in rocks is around 0.05 ppm but this raises to 0.5 ppm in superficial soil. This is most certainly due to the development within the biosphere of specific mechanisms suitable to accumulate this necessary element. Hence, if selenium unfortunately escaping from a waste repository would reach the soil, it may stay there. There is only 10 000 kg of stable Se in the upper soil of an area of 100 km^2. That would mean an isotopic dilution by a factor of 20. In that case the mean available Se for biota would have an activity of 10 MBq/g. Of course, this is a far–fetched and not so likely scenario, since Se would have to escape completely and be captured totally by the upper soil. Nevertheless, it would be wise seeking a better knowledge of the Se cycle and its distribution in living matter.

For all these considerations, the potential for non-homogeneity is a capital question, and this has prompted an important part of the new experimental research programme initiated by IRSN: the ENVIRHOM programme.

This programme associates research on both environmental and human protection. This is because: firstly, there are permanent interactions between man and the biosphere; secondly because man is a mammalian that is studied mainly with animal models; and last because experimental tools (safe radioactivity manipulation in the laboratory, analytical devices etc...) are similar in both cases.

As regards to the environmental part of the programme, the first priority is to study what is specific to chronic exposure. Indeed, it is possible that chronicity and low level doses would induce different biokinetic parameters. Since there is time for redistribution in the whole ecosystem and for changes in speciation, there is also a chance for bioaccumulation, either in specific components of ecosystems, in specific plants or animals, or in specific cells or even sub-cellular structures. There are well-known examples of bioaccumulation (or even biomagnification) such as iodine in the thyroid or mercury in top marine predators.

The first objective will be the search for bioaccumulation situations. This leads to studying more deeply transfer mechanisms, especially in relation with speciation across biological barriers. The second objective will address the search for indications of malfunctioning when bioaccumulation does occur, either at cell level, global ecosystem level or intermediate level.

This programme is conducted with a small number of biological models: algae, plants, mollusks, fish and rodents, the last also being used as a model for man. The radionuclides under scope are those that have the greatest chance to bioaccumulate: U, Am, Np, Pu, I, Po, Th, Tc, Cs, the last of this list being the negative reference.

The programme is running since the beginning of 2001 with a first focus on U and Cs and a current manpower of about 20 people, a figure expected to further grow in the future if the first steps are successful.

Figure 1. **U incorporation by unicellular algae (experimental illustrations)**

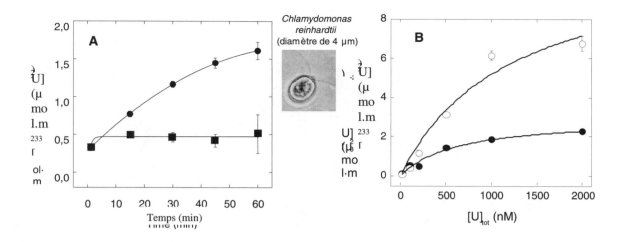

Some results have already been acquired for the algae model. This is a typical example of what happens when a chemical species crosses a biological barrier, in this case the cell membrane. The cells are first placed in a nutrient solution where the uranium concentration is imposed. Figure 1A shows the time evolution of the concentration inside the cells (circles) and at their surface (squares, lower curve). Figure 1B shows what happens after 30 minutes of exposure as a function of the U concentration, with the upper curve having been obtained at a pH of 5 (open circles), and the lower curve at a pH of 7 (closed circles). It is clear that the relation is not perfectly linear, and more important, that the external pH strongly influences the transfer by a factor of up to 4. For uranium, this is clear evidence that the transfer rate is depending on the chemical species being transferred.

It is very likely that if additional parameters are simultaneously further changed, the range of variation of the transfer factors will be even greater. This has been confirmed by experiments conducted in real water from a French river cross-contaminated with cadmium and zinc: according to the presence or absence of this cross-contamination, the transfer factor to aquatic organisms of radioactive contaminants (Cs, Co, Ag) was varied by a factor of 2.

In the case of unicellular algae, there is only one interface to cross from the outer medium to the inner cell volume. In real ecological situations, the toxicant will be faced with many different interfaces to cross before reaching its target, and each interface is prone to increase the variability of the overall transfer. It is hence not surprising that the overall transfer between the original source and the final target may prove to extend over several orders of magnitude.

Figure 2. **Various animal models used in the scope of the analyses of the multi-pollution context. On the left Corbicula fluminea, in the middle, Dreissena polymorpha and on the right the rainbow trout (Oncorhynchus mykiss)**

Similar experiments are performed at IRSN with multicellular organisms: small mollusks, fish (Figure 2)…

In parallel, work is also carried out on the soil-plant system. The root transfer, which is nearly negligible in the case of an acute foliar contamination, may lead to important redistributions with time in a chronic contamination situation. The modeling approach to this root transfer understanding is continuously improving. Initially, it was a simple linear transfer between a mean soil compartment and a mean plant compartment. During the PEACE European program that is now completed, a distinction was made between the soil itself and the interstitial water, which proved to be of paramount importance in governing the transfer to the plant. Currently, the BORIS subsequent European program distinguishes now 3 sub-compartments of the soil: the mineral part, the organic part and micro-organisms, which are prone to influence contaminants speciation (and therefore subsequent transfer).

Table 1. **Simplified presentation of the main processes bringing soil micro-organisms into action, and expected repercussions on the availability of elements with long life radio-isotopes. Processes induced by mycorhization, not documented for these elements, are not included in the table**

Radionuclides in the form of		cation(s)					anion(s)		
Process		Am	Pu	Ra, Th	Cs		Iodine	Tc	Se
Rhizosphere acidification	↗	◆◆◆	◆◆	◆	◆	↘	◆	◆	◆
Production of chelating compounds	↗	◆◆	◆◆	◆◆		↗↘ ?	◆◆◆	◆	◆
Biosorption and bioaccumulation	↘?	◆◆	◆◆◆	◆◆	◆◆◆	?			
Contribution to colloidal transport	↗?	◆◆	◆◆	?	?	?			
Decomposition of organic complexes	↗?	◆◆	◆◆	?	?	↗↘ ?	◆◆	◆	◆
Microbial reduction of the element	↦					↘		◆	◆◆
Microbial oxidation of the element	↦					↗			◆◆
Formation of Fe, Mn hydroxide	↦					?			◆◆
Bacterial reduction of Fe, Mn	↦					?		◆◆◆	◆◆
Formation of sulphurs (coprecipitation)	↦					↘		◆◆	◆◆
Biomethylation from the soil	↦					↗↘ ?	◆◆		◆◆◆

◆	–	known (or likely) process whose significance is qualitatively hierarchised from ◆ (slight significance) to ◆◆◆ (extremely significant)
↗ (↘)	–	process will tend to increase (decrease) mobility in the soil / root transfer
↦	–	the process is improbable or non existent (or its effect is negligible with respect to the other mechanisms)
?	–	the process (or its repercussions) is (are) not documented or very little documentation exists

An extensive bibliographic search has been carried out to identify processes that may be of importance. Not surprisingly, some of these processes, particularly in the case of exotic radionuclides (such as Am, Pu, Ra, Th, I, Tc, Se, Table 1), are poorly documented.

The experimental work recently initiated is to include column experiments. The first experiments (figure 3) with a closed system show that the soil organic content has a strong influence on oxygen consumption. It is hence very likely that other processes will also be modified.

Figure 3. **Soil oxygen consumption in a closed system according to the soil organic content**

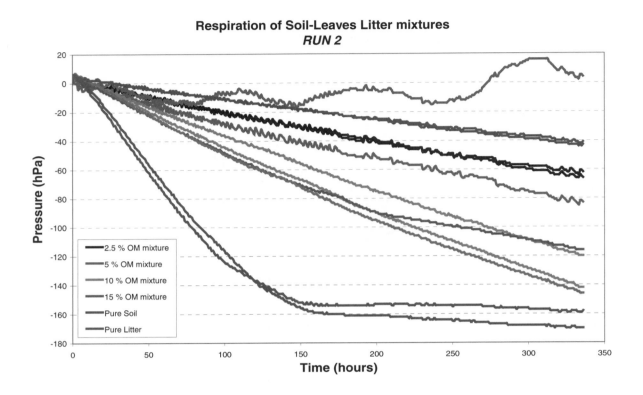

Global systems

In ending this review of current experimental work at IRSN, it is important to underline the usefulness of a simultaneous handling of the biosphere, the upper geosphere and the deeper geosphere.

The biosphere, including atmosphere, oceans and the upper soil is a nearly closed system. Inner exchanges are much more important than exchanges with the geosphere. The carbon cycle, for example, is typical of a rapid mixing within the biosphere. For the atmosphere to equilibrate with the continental biomass, it takes only a few tens of years, and a few hundred years to equilibrate with oceans. Other biogeochemical cycles are less known, especially for oligo-elements. It is likely that the biological processes responsible for cycling are able to make a partition between useful elements that remain bioavailable and toxic elements that are put aside from cycles or eliminated towards deeper soil or sediments.

Processes that allow a global loss of "toxic" elements are hence particularly important to identify. In some cases, infiltration of water is one such phenomenon since, when the water is out of reach for biological pumping, the potential for reintegrating biological cycles is very low.

In order to study this very important transition zone between soil and underlying rocks, IRSN has installed experimental parcels in the vicinity of Chernobyl, in the most contaminated area.

The upper soil layer was removed and replaced by a clean one on which vegetables have been sown. It was then ready for a new contamination, smaller than the initial (accidental) one but perfectly controlled.

A first experiment was to contaminate with radioactive iodine and chloride. Three months after contamination there was no significant move of iodine. But only one month after, chloride was totally washed off. This example demonstrates that there is no serious risk of persistent contamination of the biosphere with chloride 36 in the case of a leakage from a waste storage. Conversely, iodine is prone to accumulate in the biosphere. Experiments are still underway to clarify the rate of iodine transfer.

Another series of experiments is devoted to the study of migration. For this purpose, we took advantage of an existing trench filled with wastes coming from the red forest. This trench is a source of radionuclides that may contaminate its surroundings.

Figure 4. Scheme of the trench filled with radioactive wastes that is exploited for migration studies

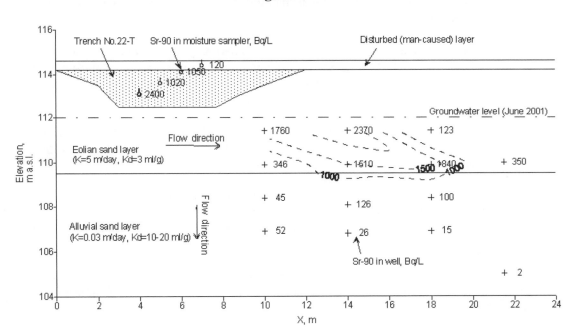

The important result is that migration remains small even in the case of a mobile radionuclide (strontium) in a very permeable sand. The horizontal motion is not exceeding 15 m in 15 years within the eolian sand layer. In the alluvial sand layer, which corresponds to the saturated zone, the contamination transfer is nearly stopped.

This experiment clearly demonstrates that the biosphere does not necessarily act as a trap for contamination and that return to the biosphere after an escape may prove to be very difficult.

Environmental modelling

At IRSN, modelling is conducted in close connection with experimental work. The first generation of operational models was mainly designed for accidental situations. These were simple but sufficient in such cases where a few phenomena and a few elements are dominating.

Some variants of these models can handle continuous releases and are used to evaluate radioactive impact of power generating plants. They are able to evaluate the concentrations in critical compartments of the environment, and to indicate where some traces of radioactive contaminants may be found.

However, these existing models are not adapted to the appreciation of a global and long-term impact in chronic situations. For this purpose, a new generation of models will be necessary.

First, for use in the long-term, a perfect balance of the fluxes is necessary. All that comes in a compartment has to leave another. This is mandatory since the resultant trend of the cycling phenomena may be small as compared to the amplitude of the oscillations. Modeling cannot hence be limited to some important compartments, it has to handle the whole system, at least up to a boundary where the fluxes are known.

Second, these models will have to handle situations where none of the stressors is dominating and where radioactive transfer are depending not only on the presence of other contaminants but also on the ecological context, including the anthropogenic pressure. This leads to include in the models a correct representation of these phenomena.

It would not be realistic of course to try to build on the spot such a "universal" model, but it is possible to gather and orient the forces to progressing towards this aim. This is the philosophy pursued at IRSN with the "SYMBIOSE" program.

The immediate aim of this program is to concentrate on radioactivity impact, on quality and ergonomy of codes, still without including, in a first phase, all other stressors. But this initial and necessary work will be done within an overall structure compatible with future improvements and later additions.

All unnecessary approximations that prevent the reaching of perfect flux balances will be avoided. Analytical formula whose validity was restricted to particular cases (transient or stationary) will be replaced by exact resolutions.

The environment is represented by means of boxes that can communicate. The level of description may be adjusted according to the need (and of course to the level of knowledge). This kind of representation allows any kind of refinement as soon as new knowledge becomes available. The boxes can also be split in smaller boxes allowing for new processes to be added.

Current developments will illustrate this strategy in the case of biomass contamination after an accident. In this situation, the first and main phenomenon is the contamination deposit on leaves. Existing models are able to take into account the foliar surface in order to estimate this deposit. But the subsequent events are usually estimated with important approximations. Roughly, the biomass concentration is made to decrease exponentially, a feature supposed to simulate the dilution due to biomass build up.

In the new generation of models for example, it will be necessary to include a more precise sub-model of the biomass increase, which would account for the main factors influencing growth, such as rain and solar radiation, as a minimum.

At a later stage, the next step will be to include also the potential effect of additional chemical stressors on biomass build up.

Conclusion

We know a lot on acute and large impact but nearly nothing about chronic and small impact. We are not yet able to resolve whether a change is a fluctuation that will have no serious consequences, or the start of a catastrophic evolution.

It is clear that radioactivity is only one among a number of other stressors, and certainly not the primary one, except for large accidents. Since living organisms, and even the biosphere as a whole, react to the entirety of their surroundings, it is necessary to take all this into account in a holistic way. This means caring about the effects of usual toxicants in addition to radiotoxicants of course, but also about effects of other cofactors such as nutrients availability and ecological interactions between biota.

It is hence necessary to conduct research in a real pluridisciplinary way. It is time to level out past boundaries that have existed between radioecology and ecotoxicology, which are both integral parts of ecology. The radioprotection of the environment cannot be separated from the overall protection of the environment, and as such should not be addressed as a stand-alone objective.

CONCEPTS, METHODS AND MODELS TO ASSESS ENVIRONMENTAL IMPACT

R. Jan Pentreath

Environmental Systems Science Centre, University of Reading, United Kingdom

Abstract

The environmental impact of chemicals generally in the environment is a subject that has been approached in recent years in ways that are different in concept and practice. They range from chemical "toxicity" and "residual" risk assessments based on individuals, to broader based, ecological risk assessments. At the same time, approaches to considering what in the environment should be protected, and how, has also changed. Approaches to this subject vary from strict conservation of identified species and areas, to the more general concepts of wishing to maintain the biological diversity within and amongst all species and habitats, and of protecting large habitat areas against irreversible human damage.

Against this background, approaches to the issue of the possible impact of radionuclides in the environment over the last decade or so have centred around the various statements made by the ICRP; either attempting to support them, or seeking to compensate for their perceived deficiencies. There have been arguments that, because man is an integral part of "the environment", and is afforded such a high level of protection, then all other components of it would be axiomatically protected. There have also been calculations to demonstrate that, in hypothetical situations, if radionuclide concentrations in the environment were such that the 1mSv a^{-1} dose limit to man was not exceeded, then the concentrations of radionuclides in the animals and plants in their food chain would therefore receive dose-rates less than those likely to cause them "harm" at the population level.

Some countries have been more direct. In the USA, dose "standards" for the protection of populations of all aquatic animals have been introduced, and consideration is being given to the introduction of dose "standards" for populations of all terrestrial plants and animals. The introduction of a set of "no effects" dose-rate screening reference levels for different types of fauna, to be applied to individual sites, is also planned in Canada.

A somewhat conceptually different approach is that of an attempt to develop a hierarchical system for environmental protection based on a narrowly defined set of Reference Fauna and Flora – analogous to that of Reference Man – consisting of defined dose models, data sets to estimate exposures, and data on biological effects, to provide a set of "derived consideration levels" of dose-effect relationships for individual fauna and flora that could be used to help decision making (along with other relevant biological information) in different circumstances.

Research work is also underway to produce systematic frameworks – also using a "reference fauna and flora approach" – for assessing environmental impact in specific geographic areas, such as European and Arctic ecosystems.

1.   Introduction

There are many different approaches to protecting the environment from all manner of stresses and strains that are placed upon it, and all of these approaches can be regarded as different facets of environmental management generally. It is therefore useful first to consider, very briefly, this broader framework because it is at the margins – the interfaces – of its constituent parts that many difficulties arise. This is particularly the case when attempting to rationalise the different concepts that underlie them, and to satisfy the legislative requirements that may then emerge. With regard to its biotic component, this broader framework of environmental management may be regarded as including:

- **environmental exploitation**, which includes such activities as fisheries, forestry, and so on, where the aim is to "crop" sustainably, specific populations of animals or plants;

- **conservation and protection of the natural environment**, which may include the requirement to afford protection at the level either of the individual or of the local population of particular species, or of habitats, or of entire ecosystems; and

- **pollution control**, often also referred to as "environmental protection", but which is essentially practised in order to safeguard the human population and to meet the requirements of other forms of environmental management or protection, and which is usually achieved by reference to various forms of "environmental quality standards" that relate either to human health, or have been derived via some form of "toxicity test" basis in order to protect wildlife.

These are not the only facets of environmental management: others include, for example, the management of natural resources such as fresh water, or the impact of extreme natural conditions, as in flood defence. But the above three categories – in relation to the biotic environment – are sufficient to demonstrate that the demands arising with regard to the control of ionising radiation are essentially the same as those arising from other forms of "pollution control". They therefore have to meet, explicitly and often legislatively, the requirements that stem from the need to manage the sustainable exploitation of natural resources, and those that arise from the conservation of the natural environment. They therefore also have to meet the needs of society generally, bearing in mind that these, too, arise from different ethical and moral outlooks, as recently discussed by the IAEA (IAEA, 2002).

Thus the **exploitation of natural resources** is usually – but not always – based on the public acceptance that individuals in the "cropped" population will die; concern is therefore centred on the numerical maintenance and "welfare" of the population. But populations do not exist in isolation, and thus there is an increasing tendency to consider the management of such activities in a broader – habitat or ecosystem – management context.

Nature conservation is somewhat different; and it is also a changing subject. The trend nowadays is to try and maintain biodiversity and protect habitats, rather than to place the emphasis on the conservation of rare and endangered species. Biological diversity includes the diversity to be found within species, amongst species, and amongst habitats. The need to maintain it therefore encompasses all living things. Similarly, "habitat protection" can encompass a wide variety of fauna and flora, both common and rare. Many species, in many countries, are afforded protection against wilful destruction at the level of the individual, irrespective of their abundance in any particular area. This is often as much a reflection of societal views as it is a result of scientific analysis of the actual risks to the wildlife concerned. And because the concept of "conservation" is centred around the need for active management in order to achieve a given environmental outcome, the requirements of others to contribute to it vary considerably from place to place and from time to time. Large areas of the environment may be "designated" in order to achieve such outcomes. Thus, for example, within the European Union designations under two EC Directives (EEC, 1979, 1992) have resulted in the Natura 2000 sites that have to be maintained in, or restored to, "favourable conservation status". Such areas are still being designated, but in Great Britain alone they already include about 2.5M hectares and may yet extend further. They can, potentially, include any area up to 200 miles seawards from the shore, and any licensed activities related to them need to be assessed with regard to their potential impact, and specifically in relation to the criterion of "favourable conservation status".

Pollution control has also had to meet these challenges, as well as those arising from human health needs. The basic tools of pollution control have not changed greatly, but the concepts behind them have. No longer is the concept of "dilute and disperse" an acceptable one. Instead the emphasis is on minimising the need to end up with any form of waste at all in the production cycle; plus the need to deal any waste that nevertheless remains by using the best available technology to ensure that the environment will not be "harmed" as a result of any emissions from a site or residues left on it. This assurance is usually reflected in one or more assessment procedures based on different forms of "effects analysis".

2.   Typical assessment techniques for pollution control

As to be expected, there are many and continually evolving ways in which pollution control methods and models are derived but, again for the purposes of this paper, the following general categorisation may be useful.

Chemical risk (toxicity) assessments

Many of the earlier studies to assess the potential "harm" of chemicals to both man and fauna and flora were made using simple toxicity tests. They were "simple" in that the data recorded were relationships between (a) the concentration of one or more chemicals in food, in the ambient medium (air or water) – or even in an injected fluid – and (b) an observed effect in the target organism (early death, cancer induction, sterility, or whatever). But such quantitative chemical risk assessments, particularly in relation to mammals, are now considerably more advanced and are centred around the derivation of data in relation to "mode of action" and "tissue dosimetry" (e.g. Andersen & Dennison, 2001). The former uses pharmakokinetic (PK) models to describe the fate of chemicals within the body, and the latter uses pharmakodynamic (PD) models to specify the relationship between the dose, however expressed, and the changes within cells and tissues that ultimately result in an adverse biological response. When such models are based on, and applied to, the relevant basic biological data of particular species they are said to be "physiologically based" (PB). Hence one has both PBPK and PBPD models. When combined, these are often referred to as biologically-based dose-response (BBDR) models. Such models are typically used to test new and existing chemicals on rodents, particularly with respect to the induction of tumours. The results relate to effects on individuals. Our knowledge of the effects of radiation on man is derived from what are essentially BBDR models.

Ecological risk assessments

A rather different, but complementary, approach is that of ecological risk assessment in which models are used to describe the transport and fate of chemicals through the environment in order to estimate the exposure to, and effect on, major environmental components. Such models can be very general or site specific. The purpose, however, is usually – but not necessarily – to assess effects at the "population" or "ecosystem" level. But such an assessment has, nevertheless, to be based upon data that relate "exposure" of some identified types of organisms to one or more chemicals, and the resultant observed "effects" upon them. Ecological risk assessments are used when more than one medium is involved – such as for discharges to air that may ultimately affect both terrestrial and aquatic environments. The US EPA, for example, specifically requires that "residual risks" – those that remain following the mandatory implementation of technology-based controls on the emissions – be assessed for hazardous air pollutants across more than one medium. Various "ecotoxicity" values may be applied in ecological risk assessments including "no observed adverse effects levels or concentrations" (NOAELs or NOAECs) or "lowest observed adverse effects levels or concentrations" (LOAELs or LOAECs) for sensitive species that are used to represent, or act as "sentinels" for, the particular population or community that is being afforded protection (e.g. Efroymson & Murphy, 2001).

3. Approaches to protecting the environment with respect to ionising radiation

In contrast to most other forms of pollution control, that relating to ionising radiation has centred uniquely on protection of human beings, the issue of environmental protection being essentially finessed by the now well-known and oft-quoted statements of the ICRP. But this has, nevertheless, brought with it many problems and thus a variety of ways to address them. They can usefully be divided into two broad approaches:

- those that have assumed, or try to prove, that the ICRP statements are essentially correct; or

- those that have used separate dose rate limits, or some other approach, to demonstrate independently and explicitly that the environment can and will be protected.

The most basic of the former are those who still argue that, because man is an integral part of "the environment", and is afforded such a high level of protection, then all other components of it are **axiomatically protected**. This approach also often tacitly assumes that man is probably the most radiosensitive species, and that he is afforded protection at the level of the individual. Criticisms raised with regard to this approach include the fact that, even if humans are present in a given environment, they are unlikely to receive the highest doses because of the spatial distribution of radionuclides, and because of the differences in the biological accumulation of radionuclides by different fauna and flora. In fact, because the human way of life is so different from that of other animals, the human population is probably one of the least exposed of the fauna and flora living in an area where radionuclides are likely to be released. But more importantly, in terms of a generalised approach, it fails because there are sectors of the environment where man does not live (underwater) and circumstances where he may be removed for his own safety (intervention) but the fauna and flora remain.

To explore this position further, some calculations have been made in the past to demonstrate that, in hypothetical situations, **if** radionuclide concentrations in the environment were such that the 1mSv per year dose limit to the public were not exceeded, then the concentrations of radionuclides in the animals and plants in their food chain would therefore receive dose rates less than those likely to cause them "harm" at the population level (IAEA, 1992); but many of the organisms that would be exposed to radionuclides in the environment do not form part of the human food chain. The greatest weaknesses inherent in such approaches is, however, the fact that the level of protection sought for, or afforded to, the environment is not sufficiently defined in terms of biological end points, or the levels of risk associated with them; although the dose rate calculations in the IAEA study were compared with those that were considered not to have detrimental effects at the "population" level.

Somewhat different have been those approaches that use, or propose to use, one or more environmental **dose limits** as standards in order to protect the environment explicitly. Thus in the USA (US DOE, 1993,1996) standards of 10 mGy per day are in place for the protection of populations of any aquatic or riverine animals, and consideration is being given to the introduction of standards of 10 mGy per day and 1 mGy per day for populations of any terrestrial plants and animals respectively. These values were selected by peer-review of the literature, and much of the subsequent effort has been expended on developing methods with which to demonstrate compliance with the numbers selected, under different circumstances (Domotor et al., 2001; Higley et al., 2001). A similar approach has been pursued in Canada, in that "dose-limits" are being developed, albeit on a somewhat different basis. It involves the consideration of unreasonable risk and adopts what one might regard as an ecological-risk-assessment methodology (Thompson & Chamney, 2001). Several obvious questions again naturally arise with regard to both of these approaches: how does one select or derive the dose limits in the first place; what biological end points – or levels of risk relating to them – do they represent; and what does one do if the limits are exceeded?

These are not easy questions to answer. One of the principal problems has been the lack of any international basis for systematising the means by which they can be asked or answered, as is the case in human radiation protection via ICRP. There is currently a lack of any international framework within which to make calculations or assumptions from the varied and unstructured data and information gathered about the effects of ionising radiation on fauna and flora generally. And there are no other equivalents to Reference Man, which has been the cornerstone of the numeric basis for human radiation protection. An attempt to develop such an overall "system" for environmental protection, based on a narrowly defined set of **reference fauna and flora**, and consisting of data on dose-effect relationships for them, plus defined dose models and data sets to estimate exposures that could be used as a basis for decision making (along with other relevant biological information) in different circumstances has therefore been proposed (Pentreath, 1998, 1999, 2001, 2002) and supported by the IUR (Strand et al., 2000). A number of developments to produce such frameworks – using a "reference fauna and flora approach" – are indeed now under way for assessing environmental impact of ionising radiation in specific geographic areas, such as the European mainland (FASSET: Framework for Assessment of Environmental Impact) and the Arctic (EPIC: Environmental Protection from Ionising Contamination in the Arctic) respectively.

Not that such approaches are themselves without criticism. Thus the difficulties with attempting to develop a systematised Reference Fauna and Flora approach include the potential scale of the task, and the extent to which it could usefully be applied to many different locations or circumstances. A rather basic "reference fauna and flora" approach was however once developed to establish release rate limits for evaluating potential environmental impacts of radionuclides dumped into the deep sea (Pentreath and Woodhead, 1988) and was applied by the IAEA in its consideration of redefining annual release rate limits for the purposes of the London Convention (IAEA, 1988).

4.   Discussion

It is evident that there is no single approach to pollution control in general, or to the issue of ionising radiation in particular. The assessment techniques used for chemicals include detailed study and analysis of the behaviour and effects of individual chemicals on individual "test" species, as well as the modelling of the dispersion of chemicals in the environment and their likely consequences. For radionuclides, the only "test species" is effectively the human being, in that such data have only been systematically collected for interpretation in the human context. Many studies have been made of the distribution of radionuclides in the environment, but primarily (although not exclusively) this has been done in order to assess the likely consequences in terms of exposures to humans, rather than to assess impact upon other species. More recently, a number of approaches have been made to address this issue, but not in any consistent way at a "global" level.

It is not necessary to rehearse here all of the issues and suggestions that have been made in the now substantial literature on this subject, but the following points are of interest, particularly in relation to the need to have and display confidence in the future regulation of the nuclear industry, and the regulators' self-asserted belief that its decisions are strongly based on sound science and defensible and logical conclusions.

- The existing ICRP statements are limited in their coverage, and do not apply in all operational or environmental circumstances.

- The inference in the earlier and subsequent ICRP statements (ICRP 26 and 60), and since echoed by others, is that concern only exists for non-human species in so far as they need protecting from actual "harm", or the risk of harm, at the population or species level. This is not necessarily the case in law, and in any case there have been no attempts to define what is meant by *risk*, or *harm*, or *population*, or *protect*, or any other key word in such statements. They therefore cannot be defended in any scientific way.

- Consequently, even in circumstances where such statements were intended to apply, and would be legally and socially acceptable, it is virtually impossible to substantiate them scientifically by any direct environmental observation.

- The statements are not helpful, and do not provide a defence, in cases where explicit demonstration of protection of the environment is required by other forms of legislation arising from the needs of **environmental exploitation** or **conservation and protection of the natural environment**. These could range from requirements to "protect" individual animals or plants, populations, habitats, ecosystems or whatever against their own definitions of what "protect" may mean in different circumstances.

- In virtually all cases involving the release of radionuclides into the environment, even an environment that humans also inhabit or derive foodstuffs from, the human animal is likely to be one of the least exposed to radiation because of his lifestyle and habits; other species will almost certainly always receive greater radiation exposure.

- Much is known about the radiation sensitivity of the human animal, but it is not evident that he is necessarily more sensitive to radiation than any other species – it depends upon the biological endpoint chosen to make the comparison.

- It is therefore unhelpful to attempt to use *Homo sapiens* as the single point of reference in order to protect the environment as a whole.

- Nevertheless, it would be helpful to have a means of demonstrating protection of the environment in a manner that was complementary to that used to provide protection of human beings, drawing upon the same principles, methodology, and knowledge base of the effects of radiation upon living things.

- The system used to protect man contains many elements, including some ethical considerations, objectives and principles, scientific "cornerstones" of data based upon Reference Man, plus guidance for their use, as well as a clear framework for managing the system and the revisions of it that are necessary from time to time. It is designed for use in many different circumstances, from "exemption" to "evacuation", and thus employs numerical values that range over three orders of magnitude to help manage them. It therefore also has many applications, from pre-operational assessments to normal operations, and from theoretical analyses of different options to dealing with actual accidents and emergencies. A complementary "system" to protect the environment therefore needs to be equally flexible, both because it would have to be applied to the same range of situations, and because it would need to interface with a wide range of other environmental management practices unrelated to ionising radiation.

- If a system complementary to that of ICRP was to be developed for protection of the environment then it, too, should have a sound ethical basis, and one that relates to the broader needs of conservation of the natural world independent of direct human requirements, as discussed recently by the IAEA (2002). And it should not undermine the existing system to protect man.

- One suggestion is that a system built around a limited set of Reference Fauna and Flora might serve as a complementary scientific "cornerstone" for bringing together the necessary radiobiological information. This would also require a more systematised approach to the interpretation of existing data, and a more focused approach to obtaining further data to fill the current gaps in our knowledge.

- The characterisation of dose-effect relationships in such a system should reflect the needs of environmental protection (such as early mortality and reduced reproductive success) and be set out in such a way that they could be taken into consideration when decisions had to be made under different operational circumstances.

- The compilation of such "dose consideration levels" could usefully be set out as multiples of normal background radiation dose levels, because there are no other points of reference, nor LNT hypothesis, to link the existing disjointed sets of data together, as there is for man.

- It would be useful to standardise the dosimetric models, and their environmental geometries, for Reference Fauna and Flora, particularly in order to draw comparisons amongst them and to compare different dose-effect relationships with normal background level ranges.

- There is no consistent means by which the equivalent of *radiation* and *tissue weighting factors* are expressed in organisms other than man, even though such phenomena are known to exist. This completely undermines the scientific credibility of any statements made in relation to environmental protection with respect to ionising radiation. A number of suggestions have been made: a Dose Equivalent for Fauna and Flora (Pentreath, 1999); a Biota Absorbed Dose (Kocher and Trabalka, 2000); and an Ecodosimetry Weighting Factor (Trivedi and Gentner, 2000). There are a number of differences behind these suggestions, but all highlight the point that something needs to be done about it.

- It might be useful to use Reference Fauna and Flora at "primary", "secondary" and so on levels in a manner analogous to the way in which Reference Man data are used. A number of criteria have been suggested (Pentreath and Woodhead, 2001) for their selection including: the extent to which they are considered to be **typical** representative fauna or flora of a particular ecosystem; the extent to which they are **likely** to be exposed to radiation from a range of radionuclides in a given situation, both as a result of bioaccumulation and the nature of their surroundings, and because of their overall

127

lifespan, lifecycle and general biology; the stage or stages in their life-cycle likely to be of most relevance for evaluating total dose or dose-rate, and of producing different types of dose-effect responses; the extent to which their exposure to radiation can be modelled using relatively simple geometries; the chances of being able to identify any effects at the level of the individual organism that could be related to radiation exposure; the amount of radiobiological information that is already available on them, including data on probable radiation effects; their amenability to future research in order to obtain the necessary data on radiation effects; and, most importantly – for this is intended to be a tool to aid decision makers - the extent to which they have some form of public or political resonance, so that both decision makers and the general public at large are likely to know what these organisms actually are, in common language.

- Once selected, however, Reference Fauna and Flora still need to be *described*, otherwise they would remain as unidentified "blobs". Such description, in taxonomic terms, is necessary both to assign existing data sets to Reference Flora and Fauna with different levels of confidence (depending on the extent to which they have been extrapolated or interpolated from other faunal or floral types) and in order to target further research to provide the necessary missing information. In this respect, therefore, it is necessary to define a taxonomic level that is not too narrow because of such factors as limited geographic range, and the data bases that already exist or could be reasonably obtained. Equally, however, it is necessary not to be so broad that almost any existing data, or any future experiments on almost any type of animal or plant, would serve as the reference data set. Thus characterisation at the level of *species* or *Genus* would appear to be too narrow; whereas *Order* or *Class* is probably too broad. This leaves *Family* as about the correct level (e.g. *Anatidae* – the ducks).

- It would be useful to examine existing data on radiation and its effects in order to see to what extent generalisations can be made. This, too, is an essential step in order to restore the scientific credibility of any statements made with respect to the protection of any species other than *Homo sapiens*. This can be tackled in more than one way. One is to examine what basic statements hold true when one progresses (or extrapolates) from a knowledge of effects at the level of DNA through to cellular, tissue, organ and whole-body effects level for different fauna and flora. The other is to take a reverse approach and examine what basic radiobiological knowledge that we use to protect human beings would **not** apply at higher (Family, Order, Class, Phylum) taxonomic levels, and why. [This is **not** to presume whether or not such information "mattered"; that is for others to decide.]

- If radiation protection of the environment is to achieve scientific credibility, then it will be essential to differentiate between different areas of knowledge and expertise (as between what is strictly radiobiological and what is ecological) and not to attempt to internalise such information on a presumptive basis.

- Scientific credibility will also depend upon the ability to produce an auditable trail of linked information that can be substantiated, complete with likely errors and propagated errors. The only two "measurables" that can reasonably be made in the environment itself, under "normal" conditions, are radionuclide concentrations and estimates of absorbed dose. Inferences made with regard to the environmental consequences (or lack of them) arising from such confirmable measurements have to be made via auditable trails of linked information, both from dose to likely effect (or the lack of it) and from one faunal or floral type to another.

And one final thought. Even if the current and past ICRP statements – sufficiently re-stated and the key words defined – were to have an element of truth behind them, it is difficult to see how they could be substantiated, scientifically, without going through most of the same or similar process that has been outlined above. For a subject area that has placed pride in its scientific advancement and rigour, the fragmented and ill-defined basis for making statements about the environmental safety of the nuclear industry and its regulation leaves much to be desired. And yet the effort necessary to redress the situation is small; it merely requires clear thinking and leadership. Many of the basic tools and data bases have already been compiled by the IAEA and UNSCEAR over the last three decades.

The successful resolution of this issue of being able to demonstrate, explicitly, that the environment can and will be protected, or that steps can be taken on the basis of agreed good science in cases where things go wrong, may well be a key factor in the future political, and hence public, acceptability of nuclear power programmes. It is evident that the *status quo* will not do; but it is equally evident that something can be done about it. There are sufficient concepts, methods, and models to do so.

References

Andersen, M.E. and Dennison, J.E. (2001) *Mode of action and tissue dosimetry in current and future risk assessments.* Sci. Total Env. 274: 3-14.

Domotor, S.L., Peterson, H.T. Jnr, Wallo, A., Higley, K.A., Bilyard, G.R. and Kocher, D.C. (2001) Using science, policy and partnerships to develop a graded approach for evaluating radiation doses to biota. In: *Environmental Protection Approaches for Nuclear Facilities* 2nd International Symposuim on Ionizing Radiation, Ottawa, 1999, Atomic Energy Board of Canada, pp 28-32.

EEC (1979) *Directive on the Conservation of Wild Birds* (79/409/EEC).

EEC (1992) *Directive on the Conservation of Natural Habitats and of Wild Fauna and Flora* (92/43/EEC).

Efroymson, R.A. and Murphy, D.L. (2001) *Ecological risk assessment of multimedia hazardous air pollutants: estimating exposure and effects.* Sci. Total Env. 274: 219-230.

Higley K.A., Kocher, D.C., Domotor, S.L., Bilyard, G.R., Antonio, E.J., Jones, D.S. and Sample, B.E. (2001) In: *Environmental Protection Approaches for Nuclear Facilities* 2nd International Symposuim on Ionizing Radiation, Ottawa, 1999, Atomic Energy Board of Canada, pp 58-68.

IAEA (1988) *Assessing the Impact of Deep Sea Disposal of Low Level Radioactive Waste on Living Marine Resources.* IAEA Tec. Rept. Ser., 288, IAEA, Vienna.

IAEA (1992) *Effects of Ionising Radiation on Plants and Animals at Levels Implied by Current Radiation Protection Standards.* IAEA Tec. Rept. Ser., 332, IAEA, Vienna.

IAEA (2002) *Ethical considerations in protecting the environment from the effects of ionising radiation.* IAEA TECDOC-1270, IAEA, Vienna.

Kocher D.C. and Trabalka J.R. (2000) *On the application of a radiation weighting factor for alpha particles in protection of non-human biota.* Health Physics, 79: 407-411.

Pentreath, R.J. (1998) Radiological protection criteria for the natural environment. In *Radionuclides in the Oceans*, International Conference, UK 1997, Rad. Prot. Dosimetry, 75: 175-179.

Pentreath, R.J. (1999) *A system for radiological protection of the environment: some initial thoughts and ideas.* J. Radiol. Prot. 19:117-128.

Pentreath, R.J. (2001) A systematic approach to environmental protection in relation to ionising radiation. In: *Environmental Protection Approaches for Nuclear Facilities* 2nd International Symposuim on Ionizing Radiation, Ottawa, Atomic Energy Board of Canada, pp 94-97.

Pentreath, R.J. (2002) *Radiation protection of man and the environment: developing a common approach.* J Radiol. Prot. 22:45-56.

Pentreath, R.J. and Woodhead, D.S. (1988) Towards the development of criteria for the protection of marine fauna in relation to the disposal of radioactive wastes into the sea. In: *Radiation Protection in Nuclear Energy* Proc Conf, IAEA-CN-51, IAEA, Vienna, Vol 2, 213-243.

Pentreath, R.J. and Woodhead, D.S. (2001) *A system for protecting the environment from ionising radiation: selecting reference fauna and flora, and the possible dose models and environmental geometries that could be applied to them.* Sci. Total Env. 277: 33-43.

Strand, P., Brown, J.E., Woodhead, D.S., Larsson, C.M. (2000) *Delivering a system and framework for the protection of the environment from ionising radiation.* Proc 10th Int. Cong. IRPA P-2a-116, pp1-5.

Thompson, P. and Chamney, L. (2001) Environmental protection program to be implemented to fulfil the mandate of the new Canadian Nuclear Safety Commission. In: *Environmental Protection Approaches for Nuclear Facilities* 2nd International Symposuim on Ionising Radiation, Ottawa, Atomic Energy Board of Canada, pp 131-135.

Trivedi A. and Gentner N.E. (2000). *Ecodosimetry weighting factor (er) for non-human biota.* Proc 10th Int. Cong. IRPA P-2a-114, pp1-8.

USDOE (1993) *Radiation of the Public and the Environment.* Order DOE 5400.5.

USDOE (1996) *Radiation of the Public and the Environment.* Federal Register 61(36): 6799-6801.

A MODEL ECOSYSTEM EXPERIMENT AND ITS COMPUTATIONAL SIMULATION STUDIES

Masahiro Doi

Environmental and Toxicological Sciences Research Group, Centre for Radiation Safety
National Institute of Radiological Sciences, JAPAN
Centre for Ecological Research, Kyoto University, JAPAN*

Ecological effects of environmental stresses: an overview

An ecosystem is a community of living organisms interacting with the physical environment in order that a flow of energy may lead to an eutrophic structure and an exchange of materials within the system. In addition, it changes constantly and their responses to the impacts are synergistic and deviated by the demographic stochasticity, environmental stochasticity and randomness (catastrophes, etc.), it is difficult to delineate the entirety of the actual ecosystem.

OECD Guidelines for Testing of Chemicals [OECD 1981] recommended some "single species tests" for the risk assessment of aquatic ecosystems. They include, for example, growth inhibition test of alga, acute immobilisation and reproduction tests of Daphnia, acute and prolonged toxicity test of fish, etc.

But these tests include no secondary effects which emerge in heuristic manners and might threaten the sustainability of the total system if they have crucial disorders on the keystone species and their functions in the ecosystem. Taking the precautionary consideration, 1/100 is adopted as the safety factor for extrapolating from the single-species assessment to adopt the test results to the actual environmental risk management, and in contrast, that for extrapolating from microcosm tests to natural ecosystem was evaluated from 1/ to unity [OECD 1981, CEC 1993, Nabholz et al., 1993]. To test the "ecological" impacts, the microcosm test is regarded to be much better than the test with single-species assessment.

Experimental micro ecosystem (microcosm) approach

Micro ecosystem (microcosm) is a functional and essential ecological unit that encapsulated and isolated from the outer biosphere, created as a fabrication of the replicate ecosystem, which can be manipulated by traditional scientific means of "experiment and control" [Odum 1971], and provide biotic simplicity [Bayers and Odum 1993]. Microcosms have therefore been used for the studies of ecological effects of some chemicals on the community, population and individual levels [Bayers 1963, Mosser et al., 1972, Taub 1976, Wilkes 1978, Crow and Taub 1979, Odum 1985, Bayers and Odum 1993] and Ultraviolet B exposure [Bothwell et al., 1994].

---

*   Contact e-mail address: masa_doi@nirs.go.jp

While, the ecological effect of radiation exposure have rarely been studied at the community level, and there are few mechanistic studies of the ecological effects of radiation.

Ferens and Bayers [1972] is one of the limited study on the acute effect of gamma radiation of 1 000 Gy and 10 000 Gy at the community level in the microcosms, which consisted of Chlorella sp. and two other types of algae as primary producers, Paramecium and four types of heterotroph protozoa and several saprotroph bacteria [Gorden et al., 1969]. It showed the significant reduction of net productivity and night time respiration during early succession at these dose levels, and insisted the significance of changes in interactions among community components in and after the stress period. These results are very suggestive, but their microcosms were too complicated to clarify the mechanisms of ecological responses against radiation and relationship among the impacts on each species and interactions from the direct and indirect effects of radiation.

To estimate the effects of radiation on the environment, ecotoxicological test must be developed in the same way as the tests for chemicals [OECD 1981, CEC 1993, Nabholz et al., 1993] in the consistent manner. To use for the microcosm toxicity test, experimental ecosystems are recommended to have simplicity, controllability and replicability. An aquatic microbial ecosystem [Kawabata et al., 1995, Matsui et al., 2000] is one of the options for the ecotoxicological tests of radiation, chemicals, etc. and their combined exposures.

The microcosm consists of autotroph algae, Euglena gracilis Z as producer, heterotroph protozoa, Tetrahymena thermophila B as consumer, and heterotroph bacteria, Escherichia coli DH5 alpha as decomposer. Environment is 10ml of aquatic medium of of #36 Taub and Dollar's salt solution [Taub and Dollar 1968] containing proteose peptone of 500mg L^{-1} in the tube, which is sealed firmly to prevent exchange of the materials. The tube was batch-cultured with fluorescent 2,500lx lamps under 12 hour light-dark cycle to make a circadian rhythm in an incubator at 25°C. Structure and interactions of the microcosm [Matsui et al., 2000] and interrelationships among constituent elements [Shikano and Kawabata 2000] are illustrated in Figures 1a and 1b, respectively.

Experimental results of single-species culture of Tetrahymena, Euglena and Escherichia coli are shown in Figure 2a, those of two-species culture are shown in Figure 2b, and three-species culture is shown in Figure 2c. As shown in Figures 2a and 2b, Tetrahymena could survive no more than 20 days without Escherichia coli, because it grazes Escherichia coli as its main resources [Nakajima and Kawabata et al., 1996]. And all cases in single-species and two-species cultures, living organisms died out eventually by the incompleteness of material cycle and/or energy flow as an autonomous ecology.

While, as shown in Figure 2c, three-species culture of Tetrahymena (as a consumer), Euglena (producer) and Escherichia coli (decomposer), showed a good sustainability for a year as a symbiotic ecosystem. From Figures 2a, 2b and 2c, it is known that each species has indispensable roles and essential functions (e.g. end-product inhibition as feedback regulation) for the maintenance of ecosystem, and should be regarded as "keystone species".

Responses of the microcosm to the exposure of gamma radiation [Fuma et al., 1998a, 1998b], Manganese ions [Fuma et al., 2000] and Gadolinium [Fuma et al., 2001] are summarized in Figures 3a, 3b and 3c, respectively.

Tetrahymena is known to have resistance to acute exposure, of which LD_{50} (50% lethal dose) is 4 000 Gy [Roth and Buccico 1965, Hill 1972]. Euglena is also resistant, of which LD_{50} is 170-330 Gy [Kitaoka 1989]. Comparing to these protozoa, Escherichia coli DH5 alpha is sensitive to gamma-ray exposure, which extinct immediately after irradiation of 50 Gy [Fuma 1998a, 1998b]. As shown in Figure 3a, lethality on Escherichia coli is the keystone effect of radiation exposure (<500 Gy), which may trigger a lethal response in Tetrahymena due to starvation as a secondary heuristic effect (predator-prey relationship).

Theoretical and computational simulation approach

It is crucial for the inclusive environmental risk assessment to assess the ecological and biological risks at community level (sustainability, biodiversity, etc.), population level (extinction, growth rate, carrying capacity, etc.) and individual level (death probability, growth inhibition, immobilisation and reproduction) as acute and prolonged effects.

In mathematical ecology, effects at the community and population levels are related to the demographic and environmental stochasticity and randomness, and characteristics of each population. Foley [1994] developed the extinction time model of the population by its carrying capacity, intrinsic rate of natural increase and initial number of the population members. Since intra-species and inter-species interactions are not included in the model, it is prepared for the population in single-species toxicology test. Therefore, if the species were regarded as the keystone species in the ecosystem of concern, the model may be extrapolated to the ecological risk assessment.

To take the ecological interactions into consideration, model ecosystem analyses are essential, and the above microcosm ecotoxicity tests [Kawabata et al., 1995, Matsui et al., 2000, Shikano and Kawabata 2000, Fuma et al., 1998a, 1998b, 2000, 2001] are the experimental trials for the analyses. The test microcosm is very simple that consists of only three species and habits in the closed tube. But the simplicity is not enough to clarify the synthesised mechanism, so that the theoretical and computational analyses are required to verify some hypotheses on the mechanisms of ecological functions and responses.

To analyse the behaviour of self-organised non-linear system of complexity, particle-based computer modelling is used to replicate the real microcosm to the simulated model ecosystem (code: SIM-COSM).

SIM-COSM is written with an object-based parallel modelling environment, StarLogoT (http://www.ccl.northwestern.edu/cm/). As illustrated in Figure 4, in the SIM-COSM environment, the physical environment in 0.1ml of culture medium is divided into 10,201square lattice patches. Individual protozoa is regarded as a particle, which is defined as a set of demographic parameters to regulate individual substrate uptake efficiency, anabolism yield, maintenance rate and growth rate, based on the dynamic energy budgets theory in biochemical systems [Kooijman 2000], of which concept is illustrated in Figure 5. When the biomass of the particle exceed the breeding threshold at the starting point of the cell cycle (G1-check point), it steps forward to synthesis (S-phase), and reproduces themselves as cell-division or cloning of the cell. Each particle dies when their structural biomass fell short of their lethal level. In the SIMCOSM, particles named "Tetrahymena" are assumed to follow the optimal foraging strategy [Chanov 1976, Iwasa et al., 1981], that is, they decide to stay or move from the present patch by the ratio of conditional ingestion rate (food-intake in ng/hr) and substrates required for growth. Details of the model will be shown in another article. Population dynamics in microcosm and SIM-COSM are compared directly in Figure 6.

Ecological responses of the microcosm exposed to acute exposure of 500Gy of gamma radiation and results of its computational model simulation by SIM-COSM, are plotted together in Figure 7. SIM-COSM does not only assess the population dynamics, but also a total set of demographic parameters of individuals, vital statistics of population and community as well as the environmental parameters at each time of interest. These stochastic parameters will be utilised to estimate the environmental toxicity on biodiversity, genetic succession, combined effects of stressors, etc.

It must be stressed that a mathematical and experimental micro ecosystems are just a model "which is an imperfect and shorthand illustration of the real ecosystem" [Walters 1971]. In this scope, experimental microcosm and its computational model simulation may contribute to understand the results of microcosm test from the view point of heuristic system thinking [Bertalanffy 1968].

How do we know the actual environmental impacts from simplified model ecotoxicity tests and analyses?

We should design the structures and interaction's webs as simple as possible to handle with scientific techniques. But, how do we know the actual environmental impacts of complexity from extremely simplified model ecosystem analyses?

In mathematical biology and ecology, there are much theories and models on population dynamics, stability of the ecological systems and prediction of extinction [MacArthur 1955, May 1973]. In general, "resistance" is defined as an ability of the system to avoid displacement during the stress period, and "resilience" is defined as an ability of the system to return to normal after the stress period. Mathematically, it proved that simplified system has lower resistance and higher resilience than actual complex system [Harrison 1979].

Empirically, simplified model ecosystem has less redundancy, and even a low impact is easy to trigger the detectable ecological responses (low resistance). In contrast, observed deviations are easily resume to the original condition, because the feedback mechanisms are simple (high resilience).

On the other hand, well-matured ecosystem is much redundant, and a small impact is diluted and no detectable ecological responses are expected (high resistance). While, if the impact is more than the permissive level, observed deviations are not easily resume to the original condition, because the system is so complex that the feedback mechanism may lead to the different phase of ecology (low resilience).

It follows that ecological effects observed in model ecosystem as shown in Figure 7, are not always appeared in actual ecosystem. Because actual food webs are much more complex than the model ecosystem, and loss of primary food for heterotroph species could be substituted by the secondary resources. In contrast, if any ecological effects are not observed in simplified model ecosystem, then, no observable effects are predicted in actual ecosystem.

From precautionary principle, microcosm ecotoxicity tests and theoretical analyses have much uncertainties, and it can not extrapolated to the risk assessment in the specific actual environment, directly. But these approaches will be valuable to compare environmental effects of radiation and other chemical toxicants with the consistent criterion.

Conclusive remarks

Simplified microbial model ecosystem and its computer simulation model are introduced as ecotoxicity test for the assessment of environmental responses from the effects of environmental impacts. To take the effects on the interactions between species and environment into account, one option is to select the keystone species on the basis of ecological knowledge, and to put it in the single-species toxicity test. Another option herein proposed is to put the ecotoxicity tests as experimental micro ecosystem study and a theoretical model ecosystem analysis. With these tests, the stressors which are more harmful to the ecosystems should be replaced with less harmful ones on the basis of unified measure. Management of radioactive materials, chemicals, hyper-eutrophics, and other artificial disturbances of ecosystem should be discussed consistently from the unified view point of environmental protection.

References

Bayers, R.J., Odum, H.T. *Ecological Microcosms* (New York: Springer –Verlag), (1993).

Bayers, R.J. *The metabolism of twelve aquatic laboratory microecosystems, Ecological Monographs*, 33, 281-306 (1963).

Bertalanffy, L.V. *General System Theory*, George Brazziller Publication, New York (1968).

Bothwell, M.L. Sherbot, D.M.J., Pollock, C.M. *Ecosystem response to solar ultraviolet–B radiation: influence of trophic-level interactions*, Science, 265, 97-100 (1994).

CEC (Commission of the European Communities) *Environmental risk assessment of new chemicals notified under directive 92/21/EEC*, p53, XI/509/93 (1993).

Charnov, E.L. *Optimal foraging, the marginal value theorem, Theoretical population Biology*, 9, 129-136 (1976).

Crow, M.E., Taub, F.B. Designing a microcosm bioassay to detect ecosystem level effects, *The International Journal of Environmental studies*, 13, 141-147 (1979).

Ferens, M.C., Beyers, R.J. *Studies of a simple laboratory microcosm: effects of stress*, Ecology, 53, 709-713 (1972).

Foley, P. *Predicting extinction times from environmental stochasticity and carrying capacity*, Conservation Biology, 8, 124-137 (1994).

Fuma, S., Takeda, H., Miyamoto, K., Yanagisawa, K., Inoue, Y., Sato, N., Hirano, M., Kawabata, Z. *Effects of gamma-rays on the populations of the steady-state ecological microcosm*, Int. J. Radiat. Biol. 74(1), 145-150 (1998a).

Fuma, S., Miyamoto, K., Takeda, H., Yanagisawa, K., Inoue, Y., Sato, N., Hirano, M., Kawabata, Z. *Ecological effects of radiation and other environmental stresses on aquatic microcosm, Comparative Evaluation of Health Effects of Environmental Toxicants Derived from Advanced Technologies*, Kodansha-Scientific Ltd. ISBN4-906464-05, Chiba, Japan (1998b).

Fuma, S., Takeda, H., Miyamoto, K., Yanagisawa, K., Inoue, Y., Ishii, N., Sugai, K., Ishii, C., Kawabata, Z. Simple Aquatic Microcosm for Ecotoxicity Screening at the Community Level, *Bulletin of Environmental Contamination and Toxicology*, 65, 699-706 (2000).

Fuma, S., Takeda, H., Miyamoto, K., Yanagisawa, K., Inoue, Y., Ishii, N., Sugai, K., Ishii, C., Kawabata, Z. Ecological Evaluation of Gadolinium Toxicity Compared with Other Heavy metals

Using an Aquatic Microcosm, *Bulletin of Environmental Contamination and Toxicology*, 66, 231-238 (2001).

Gorden, R.W., Bayers, R.J., Odum, E.P., Eagon, R.G. *Studies of a simple laboratory microecosystem: Bacterial activities in a heterotrophic succession*, Ecology, 50, 86-100 (1969).

Harrison, G.W. *Stability under environmental stress: resistance, resilience, persistence and variability, American Naturalist*, 5, p659-669 (1979).

Hill, D.L. *The Biochemistry and Physiology of Tetrahymena, Academic Press*, (1972) cited: Roth, J.S. J. Protozoology, 9, 142 (1962).

Iwasa, Y., Higashi, M., Yamamura, N. Prey, *Distribution as a factor Determining the choice of Optimal Foraging Strategy*, The American Naturalist, 117 (5) , 710-723 (1981).

Kawabata, Z., Matsui, K., Okazaki, M. Nasu, N. Nakano, T. Sugai, *Synthesis of a Species-Defined Microcosm with Protozoa*, J. Protozool. Research, 5, 23-26 (1995).

Kitaoka, S. Euglena. P*hysiology and Biochemistry*, Academic Press (in Japanese), Tokyo, ISBN4-7622-3601-2 (1989).

Kooijman, S.A.L.M. *Dynamic Energy Mass Budgets in Biological Systems*, Cambridge, U.K. ISBN0 521-78608-8 (2000).

MacArthur, R. *Fluctuations of animal populations and a measure of community stability*, Ecology, 36, 533-554 (1955).

Matsui, K., Kono, S., Saeki, A., Ishii, N., Min, MG, Kawabata, Z. *Direct and indirect interactions for coexistence in a species defined microcosm*, Hydrobiologia, 435: 109-116 (2000).

May, R.M. *Stability and complexity in model ecosystems*, Prinston University Press, Prinston (1973).

Mosser, J.L., Fisher, N.S., Wurster, C.F., *Polychlorinated biphenyls and DDT alter species composition in mixed cultures of algae*, Science, 176, 533-535 (1972).

Nabholz, J.V., Miller, P., Zeeman, M. Environmental Risk Assessment of new chemicals under the toxic substances control act (TSCA) , In: *Environmental Toxicology and Risk Assessment, Philadelphia: American Society for Testing Materials*, 31-46 (1993).

Nakajima, H., Kawabata, Z. Sensitivity Analysis in Microbial communities, In *Microbial Diversity in Time and Space* (ed. Colwell), Plenum Press, New York, 85-91 (1996).

Odum, E.P. *Fundamentals of Ecology*, third ed. W.B. Saunders company, London, ISBN 0-7216-6941-7 (1971).

Odum, E.P. *Trends expected in stressed ecosystems*, Bioscience 35 : 419-422 (1985).

Organisation for Economic Co-operation and Development, *OECD Guidelines for Testing of Chemicals*, Paris OECD (1981).

Roth, J.S., Buccico, G. *Biochemical Studies on Irradiated Protozoa 3, Catalase activity in Tetrahymena pyriformis W*, Journal of Protozoology, 12 (3), 432-438 (1965).

Shikano, S., Kawabata, Z. *Effect at the ecosystem level of elevated atmospheric CO2 in an aquatic microcosm*, Hydrobiologia, 436: 209-216 (2000).

Taub, F.B., Dollar, A.M. *The Nutritional Inadequacy of Chlorella and Chlamydomonas as food for Daphnia pulex, Limnology and Oceanography*, 13, 607-617 (1968).

Taub. F.B. Demonstration of pollution effects in aquatic microcosm, *The International Journal of Environmental Studies*, 10, 23-33 (1976).

Walters, C.J. Systems ecology: the systems approach and mathematical models in ecology. *Fundamentals of Ecology 3rd.edition*, Chapter 10, 276-292, W.B. Saunders Company, Philadelphia (1971).

Wilkes, F.G. Laboratory microcosms for use in determining pollutant stress. In: *Aquatic Pollutants – Transformation and Biological Effects*, p309-321, Oxford, Pergamon (1978).

Figure 1a. **Interactions between species in the microcosm**

Interactions between microbes

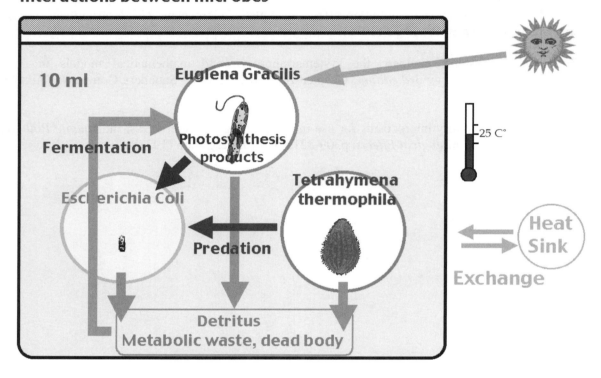

Figure 1b. **Interrelationships among constituent elements in the microcosm**

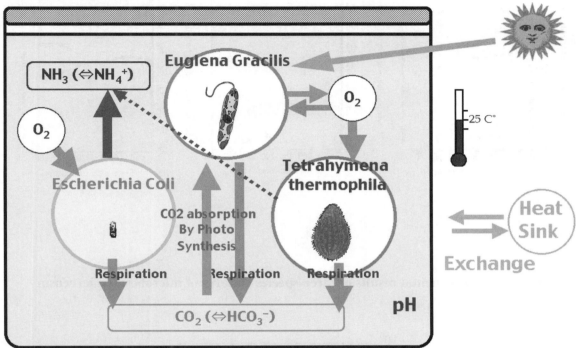

Figure 2a. **Experimental results of single-species culture of microbes**

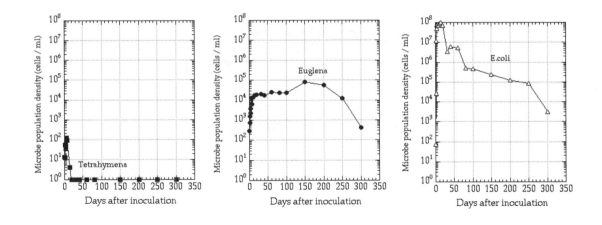

Figure 2b. **Experimental results of two-species cultures of microbes**

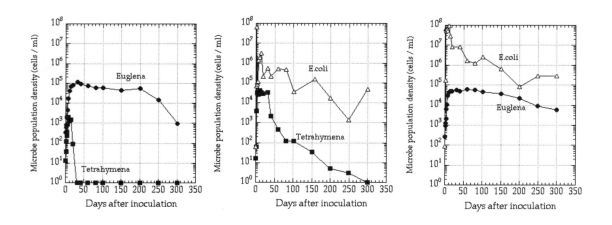

Figure 2c. **Experimental results of three-species cultures of microbes: a microcosm**

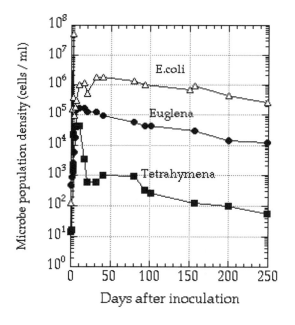

Figure 3a. **Responses of the three-species culture (microcosm) to the exposure of gamma radiation [Fuma *et al.*, 1998a, 1998b]**

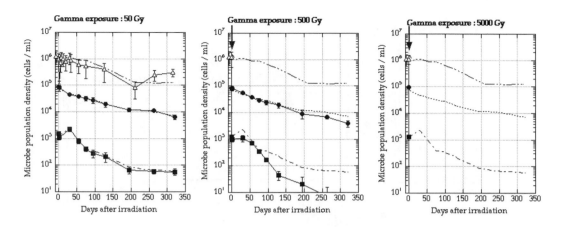

Figure 3b. **Responses of the single-species culture and three-species culture (microcosm) to the exposure of Manganese ions [Fuma *et al.*, 2000]**

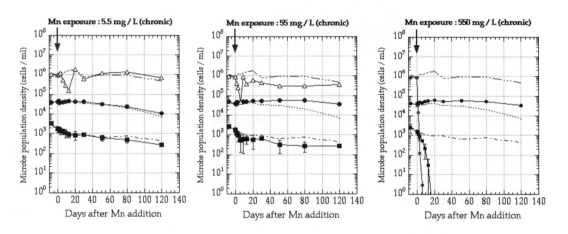

Figure 3c. **Responses of the microcosm to the exposure of Gadolinium [Fuma *et al.*, 2001]**

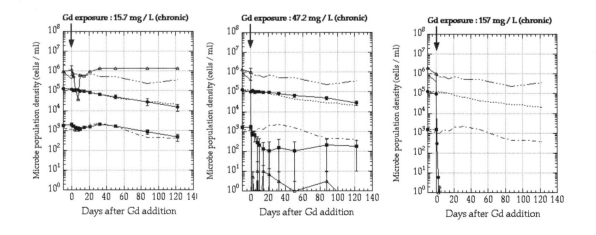

Figure 4. **Basic concept of the particle-based computer simulation model (SIM-COSM) converted from microcosm [Kawabata *et al.*, 1995; Fuma *et al.*, 1998a, 1998b, 2000, 2001; Matsui *et al.*, 2000; Shikano and Kawabata 2000]**

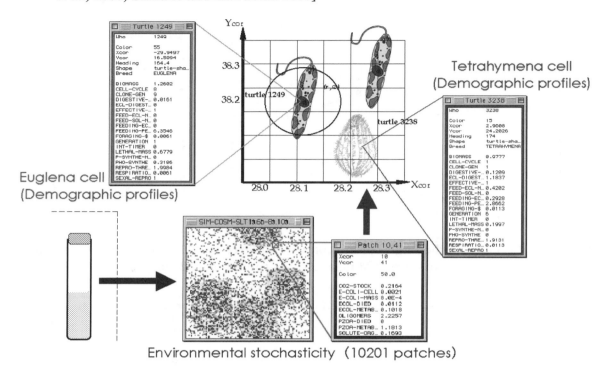

Figure 5. **Illustration of the dynamic energy budgets in biochemical systems [Kooijman 2000]**

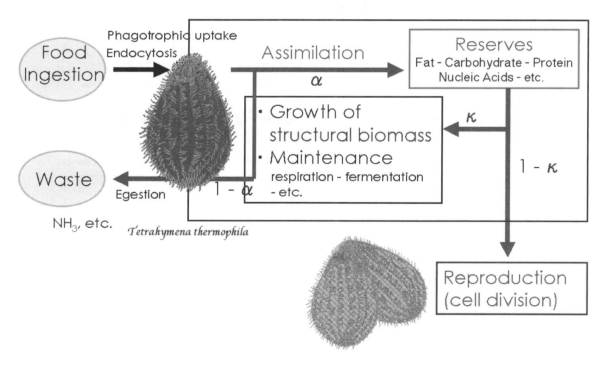

Figure 6. **Population dynamics in microcosm experiment [Fuma *et al.,* 1998b, Matsui *et al.,* 2000] and SIM-COSM simulation**

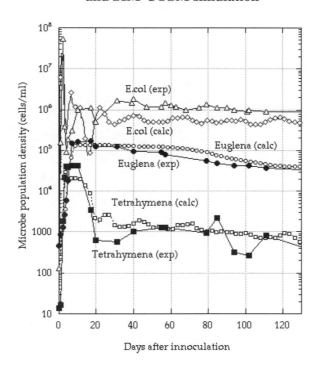

Figure 7. **Ecological responses of the microcosm and SIM-COSM simulation: acute exposure of gamma radiation: 500 Gy [Fuma *et al.,* 1998a]**

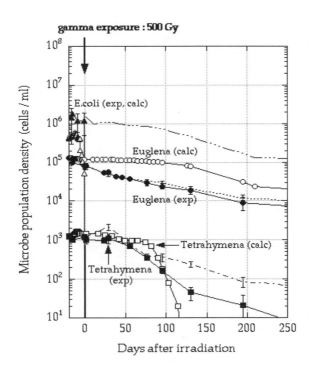

U.S. DEPARTMENT OF ENERGY'S GRADED APPROACH FOR EVALUATING RADIATION DOSES TO AQUATIC AND TERRESTRIAL BIOTA

S.L. Domotor, A. Wallo III, and H.T. Peterson Jr.
United States Department of Energy, Office of Environmental Policy and Guidance, USA

The United States Department of Energy (DOE) has been active in the development of requirements, methods and guidance for protection of the environment (biota and ecosystems) from the effects of ionising radiation since the late 1980's. This oral presentation provided an overview of: (1) DOE's requirements and strategic objectives for the evaluation of doses to biota at DOE sites and facilities; (2) a practical screening tool provided within DOE's graded approach to biota dose evaluation; (3) lessons learned from the first year of the graded approach methodology's implementation at DOE sites; and (4) thoughts for International Commission on Radiological Protection (ICRP) activities on radiological protection of the environment.

Practical and cost-effective methods are needed for demonstrating protection of biota. Through its Biota Dose Assessment Committee (BDAC), the DOE has developed screening methods, models, and guidance within a *graded approach* for evaluating radiation impacts to biota (Figure 1). DOE's graded approach is described in the DOE Technical Standard, "A Graded Approach for Evaluating Radiation Doses to Aquatic and Terrestrial Biota". A series of electronic spreadsheets for conducting an evaluation are contained in a "RAD-BCG Calculator".[1] A practical screening methodology provides limiting concentrations of radionuclides, termed *Biota Concentration Guides* (BCGs), for use in screening water, sediment, and soil media to determine if dose limits for biota might be exceeded. Methods and models for site-specific screening and detailed analysis, if needed, are also provided (Table 1). Four reference organisms were selected as the basis for methods development. Internal and external exposure assumptions and default parameters used provide for conservative screening values. Users can modify the biota dose limits and parameter values to account for site-specific receptors and exposure scenarios. DOE's proactive outreach and co-ordination with other U.S. agencies (through the Interagency Steering Committee on Radiation Standards) and with international organisations has resulted in opportunities for partnerships and methods advancement. DOE's approach for evaluating radiation doses to biota is proving useful as a sensible and cost-effective tool that could be employed within an overall framework for protection of the environment from the effects of ionising radiation.

---

1. Both are available at the BDAC web site http://homer.ornl.gov/oepa/public/bdac.

Figure 1. **DOE's graded approach for evaluating radiation doses to biota**

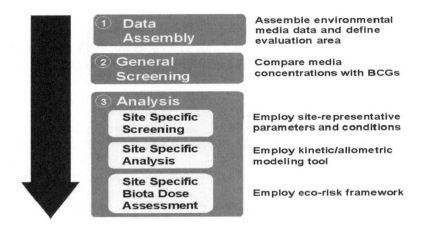

Table 1. **Summary of DOE's three-tiered process employed in the graded approach**

DATA ASSEMBLY	General knowledge of sources, receptors, and routes of exposure for the area to be evaluated is summarized. Measured radionuclide concentrations in water, sediment, and soil are assembled for subsequent screening.
GENERAL SCREENING	Maximum measured radionuclide concentrations in an environmental medium (i.e., water, sediment, soil) are compared with a set of Biota Concentration Guides (BCGs). Each radionuclide-specific BCG represents the limiting radionuclide concentration in an environmental medium which would not result in the specified biota dose limits to be exceeded.
ANALYSIS	This phase consists of three increasingly more detailed steps of analysis:
Site-Specific Screening	Site-specific screening, using more realistic site-representative lumped parameters (e.g., concentration factors) in place of conservative default parameters. Use of mean radionuclide concentrations in place of maximum values, taking into account time dependence and spatial extent of contamination, may be considered.
Site-Specific Analysis	Site-specific analysis employing a kinetic modeling tool (applicable to riparian and terrestrial animal organisms) provided as part of the graded approach methodology. Parameters representing contributions to the organism's internal dose (e.g., body mass, food consumption rate, inhalation rate, lifespan, biological elimination rate) can be modified to represent site- and organism-specific characteristics. The kinetic model employs allometric equations relating body mass to these internal dose parameters. Correction factors for the fraction of time contamination is present in an evaluation area, and for the fraction of time an organism resides in the contaminated area, can be applied to all organism types.
Site-Specific Biota Dose Assessment	An actual site-specific biota dose assessment involving the collection and radiological analysis of biota samples, using ecological risk assessment protocols.

The Department of Energy's development and implementation of the graded approach framework and our participation in international discussions regarding the need for a radiological protection framework for the environment has resulted in the following lessons learned and recommendations:

Future efforts taken by the ICRP should first concentrate on high-level "umbrella" policy and guidance that:

- clarifies and re-affirms where appropriate current ICRP assumptions concerning those exposure scenarios where "if man is protected, then biota is also sufficiently protected", and provides additional policy if there are exposure scenarios where explicit evaluations to demonstrate that biota are protected may be warranted;

- provides recommendations on acceptable effects and assessment endpoints for protection of biota; and

- considers multi-tiered approaches that include provisions for screening to demonstrate radiological protection of the environment.

A flexible and performance-based evaluation framework would allow users to work with existing processes, evaluation methods and models, and dose effects data matched to the purpose and data quality objectives of their assessment. In this regard, the ecological risk assessment framework applied in the evaluation of chemicals, with some modifications, could serve as a framework for evaluating radiation as a stressor to the environment. There are many biota dose evaluation methods and models that already exist or are under development in the U.S. and internationally that could be directly applied in such a framework.

New ICRP policy and guidance on radiological protection of the environment should be developed through a consensus-based process that reflects the balanced views of a wide range of stakeholders. New policies, guidelines, or approaches must have a sound scientific basis, and must be harmonised with and provide value-added to current policies and frameworks for radiological protection of both man and the environment if they are to be widely adopted within the regulatory community.

IMPACT ASSESSMENT OF IONISING RADIATION ON WILDLIFE: AN INTERIM METHODOLOGY FOR THE UK REGULATOR

Steve R. Jones,[1] Irene Gize[2] and D. Copplestone[3]
United Kingdom

Abstract

A methodology for assessing the impact of ionising radiation has been developed to assist the UK Environment Agency and English Nature in fulfilling their statutory obligations related to the discharge and disposal of radioactive wastes. The methodology is based on the concepts of reference ecosystems and reference organisms, currently also being developed in a number of international initiatives, and is intended as a prototype or interim assessment tool which can be used pending the outcome of current international developments. Its use has confirmed the overall feasibility of the reference ecosystem/reference organism concepts, and has identified a number of challenges, which can feed into the ongoing international developments.

Introduction

The 1990 Recommendations of the ICRP (ICRP, 1991) include the statement that "radiological control of the environment to the standard necessary to protect humans will ensure that other species are not put at risk". Over the last six years, a broad international consensus has developed to the effect that this statement, whilst it may be true in many circumstances, lacks detailed scientific justification. In addition, the overwhelming focus on human protection appears out of step with the principles of the Rio Declaration (UN, 1992), which place environmental protection *per se* as a cornerstone of sustainable development. Many have urged the development of a more detailed and transparent framework for the protection of the environment from ionising radiation (e.g. Pentreath, 1999; Strand *et al.*, 2000), and the European Commission has funded the project "Framework for Assessment of Environmental Impact" (FASSET), due to complete in October 2003, to develop such a framework.

Within the UK, the Environment Agency has a statutory duty to ensure the protection of the environment, including the setting of authorisations for radioactive discharges and the disposal of radioactive wastes. English Nature is responsible for designating, and monitoring the conservation status of, Sites of Special Scientific Interest (SSSIs), as well as other European designated conservation sites; it is also a statutory consultee regarding radioactive discharges and waste disposal

---

1. Westlakes Research Institute, Moor Row, Cumbria CA24 3LN, UK.

2. Environment Agency, Knutsford Road, Warrington, WA4 1HG, UK.

3. Environmental Research and Consultancy, University of Liverpool, Birkenhead, CH41 9HX, UK.

authorisations. During 2001, these two agencies initiated the development of an interim methodology for assessing the impact of ionising radiation on the environment, in order to assist them fulfil their statutory responsibilities under the Habitats Regulations, pending ongoing international developments through FASSET, ICRP, IAEA and UNSCEAR. This culminated in a detailed report issued in June 2001 as Environment Agency R&D Report 128 (Copplestone *et al.*, 2001), of which this paper provides a very brief summary.

Radiation effects and relative biological effectiveness

There is a very extensive literature on the effects of ionising radiation on individual organisms from a wide variety of different taxa; a smaller part of the literature refers to effects at higher levels of organisation such as ecosystems, communities or populations (UNSCEAR, 1996). Interpretation of the literature in the context of environmental protection is complicated by the variety of endpoints studied and uncertainty as to which of these endpoints would be of major relevance for environmental protection; and also by the preponderance in the published literature of studies which involve relatively high doses of gamma and/or beta radiation delivered over relatively short periods of time. For the purpose of environmental protection the effects of chronic radiation dose rates are of most interest, and it is necessary to take account of radiation types with high linear energy transfer (in particular, alpha particle radiation) as well as low linear energy transfer types such as beta and gamma.

Presently, the best considered advice on chronic radiation dose rates unlikely to harm ecosystems is that advanced by UNSCEAR (1996), based in part on earlier reviews (NCRP, 1991; IAEA, 1992) together with consideration of more recent literature. Thus chronic radiation dose rates of 40 and 400 μGy h^{-1} are considered unlikely to harm terrestrial and aquatic ecosystems respectively. The interim methodology has adopted these dose rates as reference levels, applying factors of caution to allow for uncertainty in the assessment (see below).

It is well established that radiation with high linear energy transfer is more biologically damaging, for the same absorbed dose, than radiation with low linear energy transfer. The quantity *relative biological effectiveness* (RBE), which expresses this difference numerically, depends on radiation type, dose rate, and the endpoint under consideration. Generally, RBE values for high LET radiation are greatest for low dose rates and stochastic effects (such as carcinogenesis) and lowest for high dose rates and nonstochastic effects (such as impairment of fertility). In human protection, *radiation weighting factors* are defined as a broad interpretation of the RBE data, focussing on the effects which are most important in determining health detriment at low dose rates, and are used in converting absorbed doses into effective doses for comparison with dose limits. The interim methodology defines "default" radiation weighting factors for alpha and low energy beta radiation, which are used in the calculation of doses to biota.

In human radiological protection, a radiation weighting factor of 20 is used for alpha radiation, based largely on RBE data relevant to carcinogenesis as an endpoint of concern (ICRP, 1991). In relation to protection of biota, several authors have argued that lower factors (between 5 and 10) would be appropriate, on the basis that the endpoints of ecological concern are more likely to be non-stochastic effects such as impairment of fertility (UNSCEAR, 1996; Pentreath, 1996; Kocher and Trabalka, 2000). Others have argued for continued use of the factor of 20 since this would allow also for potentially important stochastic effects such as genetic damage (Blaylock *et al.,* 1993; Woodhead, 1984), whilst a value of 40 has been proposed for use in Canada (Environment Canada, 2000). The interim methodology uses 20 as an adequately cautious "default" value, although this and other factors can easily be modified by the assessor (see below).

150

In human radiological protection, beta radiation of all energies is considered to have a radiation weighting factor of 1; however a relationship between RBE and linear energy transfer suggests values greater than 1 for beta particles with energies of a few keV or lower (ICRP, 1991). There is also experimental evidence that beta radiation from tritium (which has an average beta energy of 6 keV) has a relative biological effectiveness of between 1 and 3 for a range of endpoints (Straume and Carsten, 1993). Therefore, the interim methodology uses 3 as a cautious default value for all beta particles and electrons with an average energy of less than 10 keV, and 1 for all other beta and gamma radiations.

Dosimetric methods

The dosimetric quantity used for biota in the methodology is absorbed dose, adjusted by the above radiation weighting factors for alpha particles and low energy beta particles or electrons. In calculating absorbed doses from internally incorporated radionuclides it is necessary to calculate the fraction of decay energy which is absorbed within the organism (the absorbed fraction); likewise, in calculating absorbed doses from radionuclides in the medium surrounding the organism it is necessary to allow for self shielding by the organism. The method used is based on point specific absorbed fractions (Berger, 1978; 1981), which have already been applied to ecosystem dosimetry (Woodhead, 1979; NCRP, 1991; Woodhead, 2000), and provide a good balance between physical realism and computational practicality. The key assumptions in the dosimetric calculations are:

- organisms are represented by ellipsoids of appropriate dimensions;

- radionuclides are uniformly distributed within the organism;

- radionuclides are uniformly distributed within surrounding media, which are infinite or semi-infinite in extent;

- density differences between the organism and surrounding media, or within the organism itself, are ignored;

- absorbed dose is calculated as an average throughout the volume of the organism.

Absorbed fractions are calculated numerically using a method which repeatedly samples source-receptor pairs within the volume of the organism (Copplestone *et al.*, 2001; Jones and Vives, in preparation).

Reference ecosystems and organisms

Definition of reference ecosystems and reference organisms (Pentreath, 1998; 1999) is a necessary simplifying step in the evaluation of doses to biota, and appears to be broadly accepted as the basis for development of a system for radiological protection of the environment. The interim methodology has defined reference ecosystems for a coastal environment; a freshwater river; and a terrestrial grassland. These ecosystems are populated by reference organisms as follows:

Freshwater	Coastal	Terrestrial
Bacteria	Bacteria	Bacteria
Macrophyte	Macrophyte	Lichen
Phytoplankton	Phytoplankton	Tree
Zooplankton	Zooplankton	Shrub
Benthic mollusc	Benthic mollusc	Herb
Small benthic crustacean	Small benthic crustacean	Seed
Large benthic crustacean	Large benthic crustacean	Fungus
Pelagic fish	Pelagic fish	Caterpillar
Benthic fish	Benthic fish	Ant
Amphibian	Fish egg	Bee
Duck	Seabird	Woodlouse
Aquatic Mammal	Seal	Earthworm
	Whale	Herbivorous mammal
		Carnivorous mammal
		Rodent
		Bird
		Bird egg
		Reptile

For each of these reference organisms, the following parameters are defined:

Factor	Relevance
Ellipsoid dimensions (3 axes)	Determines absorbed fraction for internally incorporated radionuclides.
Concentration ratio (radionuclide dependent)	Determines equilibrium radionuclide concentration in organism for unit radionuclide concentration in surrounding medium.
Occupancy factors	Determines fraction of time spent by organism burrowed into soil/sediment, at soil/air or sediment/water interface, in air or in water column, etc - for the purpose of external dose calculation.
Dose per unit concentration – internal (radionuclide dependent)	Absorbed dose for unit concentration of radionuclide incorporated within the organism. Calculated separately for low energy beta, other betas and photons, and alpha to allow variation of radiation weighting factors.
Dose per unit concentration – external (radionuclide dependent)	Absorbed dose for unit concentration of radionuclide in the medium surrounding the organism. Calculated separately for low energy beta, other betas and photons, and alpha.

These parameters, together with the separately specified radiation weighting factors for low energy beta and alpha radiation, permit the calculation of weighted absorbed doses to each reference organism based on predicted or measured radionuclide concentrations in water, soil or air (Copplestone et al., 2001). For the aquatic environment, concentration ratios are specified relative to water; for the terrestrial environment, concentration ratios are specified relative to soil for radionuclides which have half-lives long enough to accumulate in soil. For shorter lived radionuclides and radionuclides such as ^{3}H and ^{14}C, for which an isotopic dilution approach is appropriate, concentration ratios for the terrestrial environment are specified relative to air.

The principal limitation of the equilibrium concentration ratio approach is the difficulty of adequately describing the scenario of ongoing atmospheric deposition into a terrestrial ecosystem; in order to do this a dynamic modelling approach is required, but at present it is not possible to construct an adequate dynamic model for all the required reference organisms. However, where measured concentrations of radionuclides in organisms are available, these can be used directly in place of values derived using concentration ratios.

Spreadsheet assessment program

The necessary calculations within the developed methodology have been coded into a program utilising Microsoft Excel and Visual Basic for Applications. For each of the three ecosystems, this program allows the user to:

- calculate weighted absorbed doses to reference organisms based on predicted or measured radionuclide concentrations in soil, air or water;

- use supplied default concentration ratio values and occupancy factors, or available site specific data, in the assessment;

- validate calculated radionuclide concentrations in organisms against measured values and/or use measured values in the calculation in place of calculated values;

- alter the radiation weighting factors from the supplied default values;

- present dose rate results for each reference organism graphically;

- carry out sensitivity analyses to explore the effect of changes in assumptions on the calculation results;

- save calculation results and input parameters/assumptions into a separate Excel workbook.

The spreadsheet program is protected to prevent changes by the user to default parameter values and the underlying Visual Basic code; all operations are executed through user-friendly menus , which ensure that calculations are carried out in a correct and consistent sequence. All assumptions and limitations are clearly stated within the spreadsheet, and the program should only be used in conjunction with the associated report (Copplestone et al., 2001).

The initial release of the three spreadsheet programmes provided dosimetric and concentration ratios for nine radionuclides (estuarine/freshwater ecosystems: ^{3}H, ^{14}C, ^{99}Tc, ^{90}Sr, ^{137}Cs, $^{239+240}$Pu, ^{238}U, ^{129}I, ^{210}Po; terrestrial ecosystem: ^{3}H, ^{14}C, ^{35}S, ^{90}Sr, ^{137}Cs, $^{239+240}$Pu, ^{238}U, ^{129}I, ^{226}Ra); the next release, due out in May 2002, will extend this coverage to 16 radionuclides (by adding ^{60}Co, ^{106}Ru, ^{131}I, ^{125}I, ^{234}Th, ^{234m}Pa, ^{241}Am, ^{32}P).

Interpretation of calculation results

As explained above, based on the conclusions of UNSCEAR and IAEA, dose rates of 40 and 400 μGy h^{-1} are used as "reference levels", which are unlikely to cause harm to terrestrial and aquatic ecosystems respectively. However it is recognised that the calculation of doses to organisms involves a degree of uncertainty, especially if default parameters, rather than site specific parameters, are being used in the calculations.

Therefore, if dose rates calculated using this methodology exceed 5% of the above reference values, further consideration of the situation is required, which may include one or more of the following actions or investigations:

- consideration of the likely radiosensitivity of the organisms receiving the highest calculated doses, and the main sources of uncertainty in the calculation for those organisms;

- additional measurements to determine site specific parameters and/or concentrations of key radionuclides in biota;

- for an existing contaminated ecosystem, initiation of appropriate ecological or bio-marker studies;

- for a prospective assessment, precautionary action to limit or reduce radionuclide emissions.

The detailed report (Copplestone *et al.*, 2001) also provides summary tables of experimental and field study data on the effects of ionising radiation to wildlife, which may also assist in the impact assessment process.

Conclusions

This interim methodology has shown that it is practicable to put together an approach for the assessment of radiological impacts on the environment, along the lines being pursued by FASSET and other initiatives. The principal challenges to be overcome in these developments appear to be:

- achieving transparency in the derivation of "reference" levels of dose or dose rate to biota, including clear linkage to endpoints and the recognition of differences in sensitivity between different taxa;

- derivation of concentration ratios or transfer factors for a sufficiently wide range of reference organisms and radionuclides;

- adequately describing the dynamics of radionuclide transfers within ecosystems, particularly for the case of ongoing atmospheric deposition into terrestrial ecosystems.

References

Berger, M.J. 1971. Distribution of absorbed doses around point sources of electrons and beta particles in water and other media. *Journal of Nuclear Medicine,* 12, Supplement 5, pp. 5-23.

Berger, M.J., 1968. Energy deposition in water by photons from point isotropic sources. *Journal of Nuclear Medicine (Supplement 1)*, 15-25.

Blaylock, B.G., Frank M.L. and O'Neal B.R., 1993. *Methodology for estimating radiation dose rates to freshwater biota exposed to radionuclides in the environment.* Oak Ridge National Laboratory, Oak Ridge, Tennessee (ES/ER/TM-78).

Copplestone D., Bielby S., Jones S.R., Patton D., Daniel P. and Gize I. 2001. *Impact assessment of ionising radiation on wildlife.* R&D Publication 128, Environment Agency, Bristol, UK.

Environment Canada, 2000. Canadian Environmental Protection Act, 1999. *Priority Substances List Assessment Report: Releases Of Radionuclides From Nuclear Facilities (Impact On Non-Human Biota).* Draft for public comments, July 2000.

International Atomic Energy Agency (IAEA), 1992. *Effects of ionising radiation on plants and animals at levels implied by current radiation protection standards.* Technical report series No 232. IAEA, Vienna.

International Commission on Radiological Protection, 1991. 1990 Recommendations of the ICRP (ICRP Publication 60). *Annals of the ICRP* 21, 1-3.

Jones, S.R. and Vives, J. (in prep.). A simple method for estimating absorbed fractions for beta particle and gamma ray photon emissions from radionuclides internally incorporated by biota. In preparation for submission to *Journal of Environmental Radioactivity.*

Kocher, D.C. and Trabalka, J.R. 2000. On the application of a radiation weighting factor for alpha particles in protection of non-human biota. *Health Physics,* 79, 407-411.

NCRP (National Council on Radiation Protection and Measurement) 1991. *Effects of ionizing radiation on aquatic organisms.* Washington, D.C. (NCRP Report No. 109).

Pentreath, R.J., 1996. Effects of ionising radiation on aquatic organisms and ecosystems. *Proceedings of an International Symposium on Ionising Radiation,* Stockholm, pp 124-135.

Pentreath, R.J., 1998. Radiological protection criteria for the natural environment. *Radiation Protection Dosimetry*, 75,175-180.

Pentreath, R.J., 1999. A system for radiological protection of the environment: some initial thoughts and ideas. *Journal of Radiological Protection*, 19, 117-128.

Strand P., Brown J.E. and Larsson C.M., 2000. Framework for the protection of the environment from ionising radiation. *Radiation Protection Dosimetry,* 93, 1-3, 169-175.

Straume, T. and Carsten, A.L., 1993. Tritium radiobiology and relative biological effectiveness. *Health Physics,* 65, 657-672.

United Nations, 1992. *Agenda-21: A blueprint for action for global sustainable development into the 21st century.* United Nations department of Public Information, New York.

UNSCEAR (United Nations Scientific Committee on the Effects of Atomic Radiation) 1996. *Effects of radiation on the natural environment.* Vol. V92-53957. United Nations, New York, N.Y.

Woodhead, D.S., 1979. Methods of dosimetry for aquatic organisms. In *Methodology for assessing impacts of radioactivity in aquatic ecosystems* (pp.43-96), IAEA Technical Report Series No 190. IAEA, Vienna.

Woodhead, D.S., 1984. Contamination due to radioactive materials. In: O. Kinne (ed.), *Marine ecology: a comprehensive, integrated treatise on life in oceans and coastal waters. Vol. 5. Ocean management. Pt. 3. Pollution and protection of the seas — radioactive materials, heavy metals and oil.* John Wiley, Chichester. pp. 1111–1287 [cited in NCRP, 1991].

Woodhead, D.S., 2000. *Environmental Dosimetry: the current position and the implications for developing a framework for environmental protection.* R&D Technical Report P350, Environment Agency, Bristol, UK.

SESSION 3

Socio-political Aspects of Radiological Protection of the Environment

Chair: Sigurdur Magnusson, Icelandic Radiation Protection Institute

CHAIRS REMARKS ON THE FOCUS OF THE SESSION

Dear colleagues, ladies and gentlemen,

It is my pleasure to welcome you to the third session of the NEA Forum on "Radiological Protection of the Environment". The focus of this session is on the **Socio-political aspects of radiological protection of the environment.**

In the session this afternoon we have three distinguished speakers. They will address what information that is needed for the development of a sound policy on environmental protection, the political imperatives and the non - radiological considerations concerning radiological protection of the environment.

We continue the session on socio-political aspects tomorrow morning with viewpoints from the regulators and the industry. The session concludes with a panel discussion.

Let me say that I look forward to the presentations of this session and the follwing panel discussion.

We as scientists attach the outmost importance to the science as compared to socio political considerations. At the end of the day however, as we heard several times yesterday, it may very well turn out that the scientific input is of relatively minor importance to the highest decision-makers in our societies when they are faced with difficult decisions to make. This we have to live with as a consequence of the complexity of our societies.

The socio - political aspects of environmental radiological protection may indeed turn out to be more important for the policy making and especially the implementation of policy than the scientific aspcets given all the external pressure and interest concerning principles of environmental protection in general and principles of sustainable development in particular.

Economical and socio - political aspects and considerations are also an important factor in implementation of radiation protection policy. Unnecessarily restrictive radiation protection standards lead to excessive use of funds as compared to the risks involved and other risks in society. Funds that may be put to better societal use providing more net benefit for society. One may very well question the social and ethical value of such standards.

This applies also to environmental radiological protection and even more so in some cases.

May I in this context remind you of one of the guiding principles of the consensus reached at the Nordic meeting on environmental radiation protection from which I reported yesterday.

There it says that:

"In addition to science, policy making for environmental protection must include social, philosophical, ethical (including the fair distribution of harms/benefits), political and economic considerations. The development of such policy should be conducted in an open, transparent and participatory manner".

Radiological protection of the environment is currently a hot and one may say "politically correct" topic that is addressed by various international initiatives that seem to be socio-politically driven rather than science driven.

This concludes the chairs reflections on the focus of this session.

THE FUTURE OF ENVIRONMENTAL PROTECTION:
A U.S. REGULATOR'S PERSPECTIVE

Greta Joy Dicus

Commissioner, U. S. Nuclear Regulatory Commission, United States of America

Good afternoon, ladies and gentlemen. I am very pleased to address this forum on "Radiological Protection of the Environment: The Path Forward to a New Policy?"

My purpose today is to describe the various mechanisms in the United States for achieving and maintaining protection of the environment; why regulatory openness and stakeholder involvement is an integral piece of a successful program for protection of the environment; and how international organisations can make a valuable contribution in providing international consensus in the global arena of environmental protection.

Before going a step forward, take a look behind you...

Before one can envision the future of environmental protection, it is important to learn from the lessons and results of the past. I believe we must examine what is currently being done in order to achieve a successful path forward. As you are aware, radiological protection of the environment is being addressed by several recent international initiatives. The International Commission on Radiological Protection (ICRP) has launched a Task Group (chaired by Dr. Lars-Eric Holm, who is on the Main Commission) to address this issue with the potential of developing new recommendations on environmental protection. As is outlined in your program brochure, the European Commission has established the *Framework for Assessment of Environmental Impact* (FASSET) project. Not to be left behind, the International Atomic Energy Agency (IAEA) has also established a work program to develop safety guidance on the protection of the environment from the effects of ionising radiation, that will take into account these and other developments.

Industry and regulatory agencies have been assessing the environmental impacts of regulated, as well as unregulated activities, for many years now. This is not a new issue. The basic underlying assumption has generally been that the environment is protected through the protection of humankind. However, I believe that in all of our respective countries, we have awakened to the fact that human impacts on the natural environment can have serious consequences. So while the protection of humankind may protect the environment, how is the environment protected from humankind? This awakening has led to a large number of corrective actions. For the most part, these actions include government intervention, such as laws, regulations, and in some cases, civil or criminal penalties. Today, with over 30 years' experience with environmental regulations, before we strive ahead to make yet additional changes to an existing regulatory framework, we need to ask ourselves the questions: What have we learned over these past few decades? And how well have these regulations worked?

The good news

The good news is that the condition of the natural environment and how we monitor and protect it has indeed improved. We know from endless studies where societies have focused on these issues that the air is cleaner, the water purer, and the land is treated with greater care than 30 years ago.

As I highlighted at last year's NEA meeting on "Policy Issues in Radiological Decision Making," NRC can very easily point to several items, that have caused the environmental regulatory framework in the U.S. to be re-visited and revised for the better:

- **Executive policy and a national regulatory infrastructure**. In the U.S., the National Environmental Policy Act of 1969 (NEPA), as amended, formulated national policy to protect the environment. NEPA also established the Council on Environmental Quality and stated that "major Federal action significantly affecting the quality of the human environment" must be accompanied by a "detailed statement" of the potential impacts of any irreversible commitment of resources. The detailed statement for major Federal actions is called the "Environmental Impact Statement" or EIS. This process allows early participation of interested parties and members of the public in the scoping process for the EIS. Upon completion of the draft EIS, the document is published, and a public comment period begins during which anyone may comment. NEPA has been implemented by NRC's regulations in Title 10, Part 51, Subpart A, and in general, provide specific information as to whether or not an environmental assessment or environmental impact statement is needed in various proposed domestic licensing issues.

In addition, in 1994, the President issued an Executive Order mandating that Federal agencies make "environmental justice" part of each agencies mission by addressing disproportionately high and adverse human health or environmental effects of Federal programs, policies, and activities on minority populations and low-income populations.

- **Consultation with other agencies**. The environmental reviews leading to preparation of environmental impact statements may involve interactions with other Federal, State, local, regional, and affected Native American tribal agencies. In the U.S., agencies that may be consulted include, but are not limited to: the Fish and Wildlife Service and the National Marine Fisheries Service related to threatened and endangered species; State Historic Preservation Offices, and local and affected Native American tribal agencies related to historic and archeological resources that are eligible for listing on the National register of Historic Places; and relevant State agencies in determining that the proposed action conforms to applicable State regulations under the Clean Air Act.

- **The process and timetable for developing regulations and supporting guidance has changed.** Years ago, complex rulemakings took many years to complete. As an example, our radiation protection regulations in 10 CFR Part 20, that implemented ICRP 26 and 30, took over 13 years to complete! Currently, through an open process and public comment period, we have been able to reduce this time to less than two years in many cases. For some multifaceted rulemakings, workshops held throughout the comment period have assisted interested parties in understanding the technical issues presented. The format of the proposed regulations themselves have changed by prefacing the proposed regulation with a question and answer (Q&A) format which more easily address the questions that are raised by the proposed actions, potentially negating the need for subsequent additional comments or questions. In addition, guidance documents have been developed and issued at the same time as the revised regulation is issued, if not before, for comment. The format for such documents include procedures that are licensee-specific, not regulator-driven. Finally, and most importantly, we have changed our regulatory framework to be more "risk-informed, and performance-based," thus allowing (in most cases) the licensees, to use detailed knowledge of their facility to determine what level of procedure, surveillance, or licensee intervention is needed for a particular regulation.

I give this brief synopsis of the NRC's transition in rulemaking from untimely and deterministic, to timely and less deterministic for the following reason. Recommendations forthcoming from forums such as this, in order to be most effective worldwide, should be implemented in a timely manner and with an open process. Countries with more cumbersome implementation processes may find this an ideal opportunity to revise those methods sooner, rather than later.

- **Improved Communications**. The NRC has learned over the years that our actions must be transparent. It is imperative that the public, legislative bodies, those most impacted by a pending action, and the media are well-informed and have a meaningful opportunity to participate in the process. By providing more clarity and being timely in our responses to interested parties, we have seen increased effectiveness in the way that we can transmit information and better communicate with the public, Congress, impacted entities, and the media. The result is the ability to resolve difficult issues in an efficient manner. Electronic communication, through the use of our newly redesigned web site (at www.nrc.gov), has proven to be extremely helpful in providing information quickly to those that seek it. I cannot overemphasise the importance of transparency.

Transparency may require a cultural change in perspectives or attitudes concerning the importance of communicating with internal and external stakeholders. Therefore improving our communication skills may be necessary. The NRC has found significantly increased positive feedback from interested parties after the staff has conducted workshops following additional training in communication skills and techniques. While as scientists, we can be extremely competent in our field of expertise, most likely we could find significant improvement in our interactions with the public if we were all able to have periodic training in effective communication. In today's world, it is just as important, if not more important, as being scientifically competent.

The not-so-good news

As you can tell by the number of Federal, State and Tribal organisations involved in the co-ordination of environmental impacts statements and environmental actions, the U.S. has indeed created a large environmental regulatory morass. I can site the familiar regulatory "discussions" between the U.S. Environmental Protection Agency (EPA) and our Agency on NRC's License Termination Rule (LTR), issued in 1997. The NRC finalised a regulation for the termination of sites that had previously been used in licensed, radiation activities: be they reactors, industrial, or medical facilities. At the heart of the matter was the appropriate residual radioactivity limits for unrestricted release of the site. The NRC established a 25 millirem (0.25 mSv) all-pathways limit, but EPA established a radiation dose limit of 15 millirem (0.15 mSv), both averaged over a one-year period. NRC, in its analyses for the regulation, relied on the findings of the ICRP and our national counterpart, the National Council on Radiation Protection and Measurements (NCRP) in using the principle of optimisation, considering the cost effectiveness of additional dose reduction. After a full review of these recommendations, as well as many thousands of comment received, the NRC adopted the limit of 25 millirem (0.25 mSv) as the value for residual radioactivity at a site under consideration for license termination. Overall, NRC's approach to radiation protection standards is to establish radiological protection regulations based on an all-pathway approach and to incorporate the application of ALARA. Most recently, NRC chose to use the limit of 25 millrem (0.25 mSv) per year limit for our draft Yucca Mountain regulations. However EPA, which has the statutory responsibility to set standards for Yucca Mountain, recently chose a 15 millrem (0.15 mSv) all pathways limit with a separate 4 millirem (0.04 mSv) groundwater standard. As required by law, NRC's final Yucca Mountain regulation adopted the EPA standard.

But what about EPA's dose limit of 15 millirem (0.15 mSv)? Isn't lower always better? Well, EPA's proposed dose limit resulted from a different technical analysis for establishing an acceptable risk to the public. Many of EPA's standard-setting authorities for radiation protection are part of umbrella statutes for environmental protection that address specific kinds of pathways for potential environmental pollution (e.g., the Clean Air Act and the Safe Drinking Water Act). EPA regulations issued under these statutes for pollutants, including radionuclides, set standards to be met and also allow the standards to be exceeded if certain criteria are met. EPA's preference is to set standards for individual pathways, which is, in part, required by its statutes. EPA chose to use a risk level, derived from its interactions and legal court decisions, of between 10^{-4} to 10^{-6} overall level of risk, resulting, in this case, of a dose limit of 15 millirem (0.15 mSv) per year. Risk versus dose. A top-down approach, versus a bottom-up approach. Two agencies with very different, but certainly manageable approaches to regulation. It all depends upon your endpoint.

Questions raised by dual regulation

The first question might be: "Does this mean that all decommissioning and license termination activities in the U.S. have stopped since 1996?" Not at all. Although our two agencies are still working on a Memorandum of Understanding for future decommissioned sites, we continue to work with EPA and its regional offices in ongoing decommissioning activities because, as you might have guessed, NRC licensees are also required to comply with EPA as well as many other regulations related to the liquid effluent discharges to bodies of water. And then, on a case-by-case basis, we work with the licensee, the interested community, EPA, as well as other State and local government agencies, to safely close-out and decommission the facility under consideration.

A second question might be: "Are we protecting the environment and the public?" The answer emphatically, from probably all agencies involved in the regulatory process, is "YES!" We may get there from different paths, but our end result and agreement in authorising any site or facility to be released for unrestricted (i.e., unregulated) use, are that the conditions for unrestricted release have been met and that there is scientifically sound evidence present in the environmental assessment or impact statement upon which to make this regulatory decision.

And finally, the third question might be: "Are these regulatory differences considered good regulation?" I am not the first Commissioner to admit that this is not the best way of doing regulatory business, but I can tell you that we are actively working on ways to streamline the process, work with our sister agencies, and to make the process as open as possible, given our scientific differences on this issue.

It is also possible that many of the countries that are represented at this conference also have similar regulatory situations such as having different agencies that are responsible for regulating and protecting the environment. In addition, I would venture that you may also have several different radiation standards to choose from, all of which contributes to the constant source of confusion and

164

possible annoyance to the public, and those we regulate as to how regulators go about performing their work. What we do know is this: There is no one overall consensus as to how to best protect and regulate the environment from radioactive emissions and potential exposure to ionising radiation. But we do have many paths (i.e., regulations), for achieving our identical desired goals, which are specifically to ensure the protection of the public and the environment we live in.

New emerging issues

In light of the growing interest in developing an integrated approach to the management of all environmental risks, the process of developing an overall policy for radiological protection of the environment should not be constrained by current national or international approaches to radiological protection, in general. To date, the U.S. has developed a national approach to issues concerning environmental protection. However, we now face two relatively new issues that have caused us to rethink about how we regulate our national radiation protection programs.

The first issue is the "clearance" or release of slightly radioactive material to the environment or commerce, which may involve the use and integration of global commodities containing small amounts of radioactive material. The second issue is closely related to the first and involves regulatory authorisation of radioactive releases to the environment and ensuring that transboundary issues between co-located countries do not arise. For both of these issues, as well as others mentioned, I believe that there is an opportunity for all of us to contribute.

The track record

We have a good track record in radiation protection. We should be proud of that and advertise that fact. Although, as regulators we cannot endorse the use of radioactive materials in commodities, we can ensure that its use, if justified, does not negatively impact the public or the environment.

Several years ago, in 1997, I believe, the National Radiological Protection Board (NRPB) contacted many countries and asked each of them to provide input into a survey that they were conducting on the various types of regulations and requirements in radiation protection, environmental regulations included. There was an excellent set of questions posed, and I surmise that it served as an excellent reference for their regulatory framework to see where the United Kingdom "ranked" if you will, with other countries that had passed similar regulatory statutes and regulations. I also understand that the International Atomic Energy Agency (IAEA) conducted a similar study, also within the past few years, perhaps for difference purposes, to gather this type of information from the many countries it interacts with the get an idea of the various levels of regulatory framework for environmental protection in existence today.

As a necessary first step in determining what any possible new system for the protection of the environment would look like, or should be, in addition to identifying what the needs of various countries may be in this arena, I would recommend that we assist the ICRP in formally gathering this information, building on previous surveys. I would recommend that we first look at the similarities and then characterise the differences between the existing various national regulatory approaches for environmental protection around the world. It may not be necessary for all countries to have identical regulations, and in fact, is probably impossible. Such a survey could serve several purposes. Perhaps for the first time, it would summarise and document all of the environmental programmes world-wide. It would collect not only the different types of regulatory frameworks in place, explaining perhaps what works best and what doesn't, but it could provide the technical, scientific, and policy bases for each type (i.e., liquid, air, or solid) of release to the environment. Finally, I note that radioactive regulations need not, nor probably should not be isolated in this survey, and in fact the information collected would assist many, in determining if both chemical and radiological releases are, or can, be regulated similarly. It may also provide options for various environmental regulatory frameworks and may result in harmonisation of chemical and radioactive materials regulations.

Such an all-encompassing look internationally may identify disparities, similarities, questionable practices, as well as many good practices and concepts amongst national programmes. In any case, base lining what each county does or doesn't do in environmental protection will tell us if there is a need for harmony (perhaps we are already there?) and whether there is international consensus to support international recommendations in this arena.

Providing perspective and gathering an international consensus on an approach to any new system on environmental protection before any recommendations are developed will go a long way to a successful conclusion. This approach may expedite overall adoption of any recommendation into national regulatory programs and legislative agendas. As an added benefit, this could also provide a sound scientific basis for any proposed changes to each country national regulatory framework and a well-documented rationale for proposed programmes. Lastly, if the results of this survey determined that very few discrepancies exist amongst the various countries, as far as protection of the environment from the use of radiation is concerned, then these findings should be published as well. It would be beneficial to the public, lawmakers, regulators, and the regulated community to know that indeed the environment is being protected through the various national regulatory radiation protection programs world-wide.

We must keep in mind that it may be that we can have different regulatory schemes, licensing and registrant requirements, but all may be achieving the same desired outcome: the protection of the environment. A general concept that protection of humankind protects the environment. It is that concept however, that we should review. As regulators and scientists we shouldn't propose recommendations or take regulatory action that would have little or no safety benefit disproportionate to the cost and impact. Again, it is quite possible that our various approaches to environmental regulation are achieving our desired goals. Is it possible that all roads may indeed lead to Rome, or in this case Taormina?

Summary

The U.S. has the largest number of nuclear installations of any country in the world. This puts us at an extreme end of the spectrum. As a result, I have touched on many issues relative to environmental protection. Therefore in summary, let me list these issues:

- Before moving ahead, look at what has been done thus far.

- Executive policy and a national regulatory infrastructure.

    - Environmental Impact Statements.

    - Environmental Justice.

- Standards determined by law or courts.

- Consultation with other national agencies and countries.

- Improving the timetable for issuing regulations and supporting guidance.

- Improved communications and training of staff.

- Transparency and flexibility throughout the regulatory process.

- Differences in regulatory approaches are OK, as long as the end result is to achieve sound national environmental and public health and safety policy.

I believe that this series of conferences represents an excellent opportunity to come to resolution about the future of environmental regulations and policies. Having this information will assist us in harmonising any proposed recommendation(s) for radiological protection of the environment involving commodities containing radioactive materials or unrestricted release of slightly radioactive materials by using the existing environmental radiation protection framework as a starting point. Doing so in an open, encompassing manner will, in my opinion, go a long way towards resolving some of the current controversies about radiation protection standards in the U.S., as well as around the world, with the desirable end result of increasing public confidence in our environmental radiation protection programs.

POLITICAL IMPERATIVES

Andrew Miller
MP, United Kingdom

Introduction

If you ask people about sunbathing on the beach, flying across the Atlantic or using their microwave, the word radiation is unlikely to be included in their response. Of those examples the most probable dangers uppermost in the public's mind are getting burnt on the beach, falling out of the sky, or salmonella from undercooked food. On the other hand Three Mile Island or Chernobyl create a different response. These are human responses that one sees in other areas of risk. Compare for example death on the road with aircraft crashes. When the latter occurs there are major enquiries that hit the headlines for several days, whilst in Europe the tens of thousands of people dying on our roads rarely justify a mention because, by and large, they occur in ones and twos at a time. So, the 2 000 people a year who die from skin cancer in the UK, largely from over-exposure to the sun, are barely mentioned because they are again individual cases. It is far too simple to either blame the media or ignorance of science, but we need to examine carefully how relative risk is communicated to those potentially at risk.

Let us look at some examples:

Radon

The natural radioactive gas radon occurs in varying concentrations in all homes and workplaces. Inhaling radon causes the sensitive cells of the lungs to be irradiated. Under most circumstances the risk is small but nevertheless, living for a lifetime in a house where radon is at the Action Level of 200 Bq m^{-3} carries about a 3% risk of fatal lung cancer (a quarter to a half of all such deaths are in non-smokers). It is estimated to be the second leading cause of lung cancer after cigarette smoking.

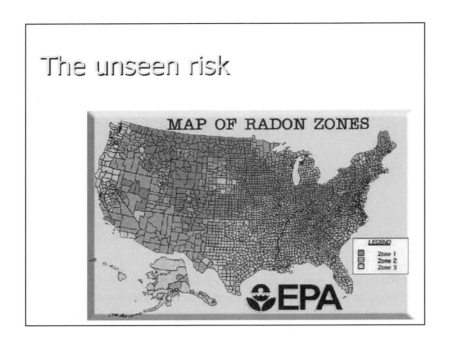

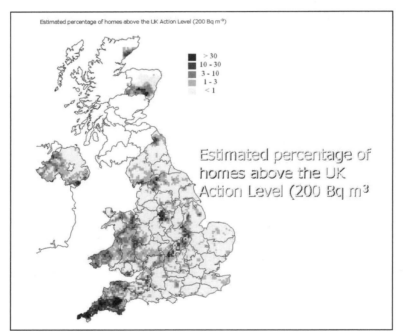

In both of these maps one can see the need for action in the field of construction, but I doubt that more than one or two percent of the population would use this data as a basis for determining where they should live. Yet if one looks at some of the research perhaps a different conclusion may be justified.

I want to draw on the work of the Radiological Protection Institute of Ireland to illustrate my point.

On 26 July 2001, RPII[1] announced:

> "Within coming weeks the Radiological Protection Institute of Ireland (RPII) is to launch a new campaign focusing on the hazards associated with radon gas in workplaces in High Radon Areas. The campaign will give effect to new legislation, implementing an EU Directive on radiation safety, under which employers may be required to measure the radon concentration in a workplace.
>
> The campaign is to begin with a pilot programme centred on Ennis, Co. Clare. Over the next month the RPII will be writing to all of the 1 500 workplaces in the Ennis area. Employers will be given information on radon and directed to have radon measurements made in their workplaces within a six-month period. These measurements can be made relatively easily and inexpensively."

This is typical of the work that is going on throughout Europe but at a political level it is not what attracts the attention of our Parliaments.

In Ireland it is far more likely to be Sellafield that hits the headlines. And yet a paper published last year by the RPII[2] said:

> "The Radiological Protection Institute of Ireland (RPII) accepts the finding of a recent study, that a cluster of Down's syndrome births in Ireland in the 1960s and early 70s was not linked to Sellafield. The study, carried out by an international group of scientists led by an Irish epidemiologist, Dr Geoffrey Dean, was reported in a UK medical journal last December. It investigated a suspected link between a serious fire in a nuclear reactor at Sellafield (then called Windscale) in 1957,"

I am not seeking to brush aside the arguments in Ireland about Sellafield, I am merely trying to put it into perspective. Again the RPII[3] are helpful here in a comment dated 5th October 2000. It says:

> "The radiation dose to Irish people due to Sellafield fell slightly in 1999, continuing the slowly declining trend of recent years. This is one of the main findings of a new report on radioactivity levels in the Irish marine environment in 1998 and 1999, which is published today by the Radiological Protection Institute of Ireland.
>
> The consumption of fish and shellfish is the main pathway through which the Irish public are exposed to radiation as a result of discharges from Sellafield. The doses received via this pathway, at 1.4 microsieverts in 1998 and 1.3 microsieverts in 1999, are a very small fraction of the dose of approximately 3 000 microsieverts received by the average person in Ireland each year from all sources of radiation."

---

1. http://www.rpii.ie/press/pr200104.htm

2. http://www.rpii.ie/press/pr200103.htm

3. http://www.rpii.ie/press/pr200005.htm

Surely therefore inhalation of radon should be a higher concern than the risk of eating prawns from the Irish Sea.

Flying

My second example is related to flying.

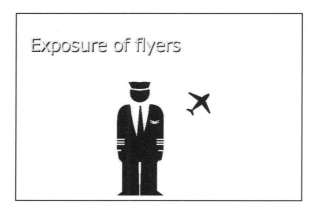

All of us have been on a plane and have been nervous at take off or landing, but has anyone ever heard a nervous passenger ask the steward about the radiation dose they are about to receive? A paper, "Assessing Exposure to Cosmic Radiation during Long-haul Flights[4]", says:

> "The assessment of exposure to cosmic radiation on board aircraft is one of the concerns of organisations responsible for radiation protection. Cosmic-particle flux increases with altitude and latitude and depends on solar activity. To illustrate the effect of these parameters, exposure has been estimated on several airlines operating subsonic and supersonic aircraft on transatlantic, Siberian and transequatorial routes. Measurements have been made with a tissue-equivalent proportional counter using the microdosimetric technique. This type of system provides the absorbed dose, the ambient dose equivalent, the mean quality factor, and the dose distribution as a function of lineal energy. Data were collected at maximum solar activity in 1991-1992 and at minimum activity in 1996-1998. The lowest mean dose rate measured was 3 microSv h^{-1} during a Paris-Buenos Aires flight in 1991. The highest rates were 6.6 microSv h^{-1} during a Paris-Tokyo flight on a Siberian route and 9.7 microSv h^{-1} on Concorde in 1996-1997. The mean quality factor is around 1.8. The corresponding annual effective dose, based on 700 hours of flight for subsonic aircraft and 300 hours for Concorde, can be estimated at between 2 mSv for the least-exposed routes and 5 mSv for the more-exposed routes."

As I understand the current position, the ICRP:

"does not consider it necessary to treat the exposure of business passengers as occupational exposure. The principal occupational group exposed to elevated levels of

---

4. *Radiation Research:* Vol. 153, No. 5, pp. 526–532.

cosmic rays is air crew. The exposure of jet air crew should be treated as occupational exposure. The annual effective doses should be derived from the flying time and typical effective-dose rates for the relevant routes. Since there are no other practical control measures, there is no need to consider the use of designated areas. It is likely that the existing restrictions on the flying time of aircrew will provide sufficient control of exposures. Pregnant members of aircrew are usually relieved of flying duties well before the end of pregnancy. The Commission sees no reason to invoke further protective measures for the conceptus."

But once again we have an example that shows the dramatic, i.e. the plane crash, has a greater resonance with the public rather than the continued, albeit small, risk of the radiation dose.

Similarly doses from nuclear power plants are a cause of much greater public concern than risks from frequent flying.

Mobile telephony

The third area I want to examine is that of mobile telephony.

Half of the UK has mobile phones but there is an argument about the placement of every mast. Although some campaigns are legitimate because of impact on visual amenity they are often associated with claims of health risk to the surrounding population. If we look at the facts from the individual point of view of the individual user, one would have thought that the heating of the brain might cause greater concern than the growth of the industry indicates.

Complex terminology such as SAR might cause worries.

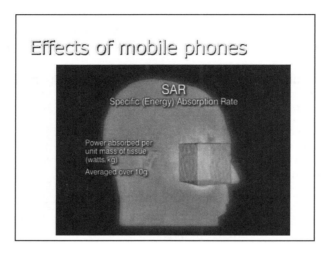

Pictures of heated brains might cause even more panic, even though we are only talking about .1°C.

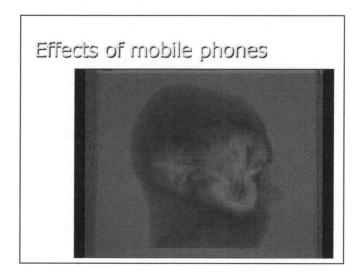

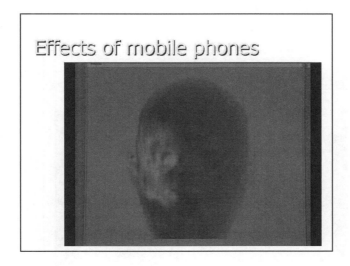

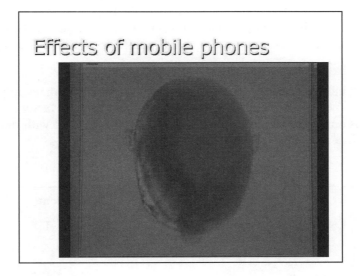

This again illustrates the way in which the human response to the radiation levels is very much driven by the concerns over the large-scale development rather than the impact on the individual. The typical response, however ill founded, is about the mast being too close to a child's school rather than the parents desire to own and use mobile phones.

The way forward

We will never arrive at a point where all decision makers, whether they are parents or Prime Ministers, fully understand all the scientific issues surrounding the key decisions that are needed. And yet everyone makes decisions about risk many times each day.

Some risk assessment is at the subconscious level such as judgements about crossing the road.

We receive basic training from parents and teachers but so much of the decision to cross is based upon a complex judgement relating to speed and distance. The formula is complex but we all do it regularly.

Some are much more conscious, like smoking or participating in dangerous sports. We know about the risk, yet many are prepared to take it. Perhaps the common factor is that we make an assessment of relative risk and that this is the best way to help people deal with radiation risk. I think Vodaphone present this in a sensible manner:

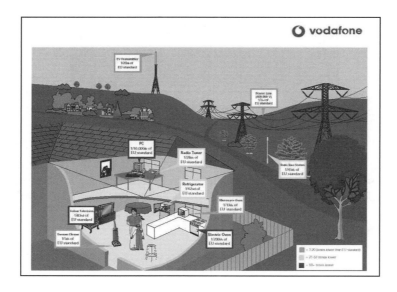

They help us gauge the relative risk from big things like masts and pylons by comparing them with commonplace items around the home.

176

The public understanding of science is best achieved by openness and honesty. In previous years all nations have been guilty of avoiding these principles. That was understandable as many developments particularly relating to radiation were classified for obvious reasons.

Radiation information relating to depleted uranium shells is in the public domain. Whilst there is a lot of controversy about the causes of, for example Gulf War illnesses (and frankly I doubt there is any general connection with DU), the nature of the ordnance used is well known. The open nature of the debate is quite new and very different to similar arguments from previous conflicts and weapons testing.

In being open it is also important to avoid scare-mongering. Let me be clear, I am not going to stop going into the sun whilst on holiday in Cornwall, neither am I going to travel the world avoiding heights over 20 000 feet. But at the same time we need to encourage considered and sensible judgements, just like those we use when crossing the road.

Conclusions

- Help citizens make informed judgements.

- Ensure the experts and politicians speak the same language.

- Develop techniques that help explain complex scientific concepts.

To enable people to make sensible judgements we have to de-mystify the language of both scientists and politicians. We also have to avoid confusion caused by different standards that have been used in various countries – in other words use debates like this to try and ensure that common standards are used. And finally, using concepts such as relative risk, help overcome very natural fears that surround radiation concerns.

NON-RADIOLOGICAL FACTORS AND DECISION MAKING ON THE RADIOLOGICAL PROTECTION OF THE ENVIRONMENT

Alan Simcock

Executive Secretary, OSPAR Commission[1]

Abstract

"Non-radiological factors" can cover both physical and non-physical issues. As far as physical issues are concerned, the appropriate course is not to forget that radioactive substances have to be considered in the same way as other substances in respect of their non-radioactive properties.

"Damage to amenities" and "interference with legitimate uses of the sea" are long-standing descriptions of the non-physical aspects of marine pollution and degradation. A framework for a taxonomy of the interests involved in such aspects is suggested, using the three dimensions of the degree of linkage to the marine environment, the nature of the interaction with the marine environment, and the economic nature of the interest concerned. Questions of remoteness also arise.

A multi-dimensional analysis of the risks to the interests concerned is suggested. The dimension of "public response" is particularly significant for the non-physical aspects of marine pollution and degradation. This dimension is complex, being influenced by "fright factors" and subject to media amplification. These influences can include special local economic circumstances and past experiences.

Finally, the process for integrating physical and non-physical factors is examined. Early consideration is recommended of how to achieve a transparent presentation of the issues and the way in which decisions are to be taken.

---

1. This paper represents solely the personal views of the author. None of the views expressed should be regarded as those of the OSPAR Commission, its member Contracting Parties or the OSPAR Secretariat.

THE REGULATOR´S VIEWPOINT

Paloma Sendín
Nuclear Regulatory Commission CSN, Spain

Abstract

The speaker recalls the task of regulators in establishing criteria and standards and assessing and controlling their fulfilment, as well as the fact that there are many types of radiological regulators, depending on their targets, structures, level of independence, and others. She also stresses that regulators take the environment presently into account to protect people as far as ionising radiation is concerned, that is, environmental protection is provided by present regulations, although implicitly based on an anthropocentric focus. In this sense, there is a clear need to develop a framework for the protection of environment, on the basis of the evolution of the present system. There is a preference for a unique, coherent, timely, integrated and manageable radiological human and environment protection system, which has to be developed internationally. Such an enhanced environmental protection framework needs of clearly defined specific "bricks" (principles/criteria/tools). Regulators will face important challenges in adapting to an integrated man/environment protection framework, and need to act nationally in the meantime to fulfil obligations, as well as actively encourage international initiatives. A proposal on a radiological environmental framework is laid down, and finally she states the overall regulators viewpoint on this process: "The path towards pragmatism and credibility".

U.S. NUCLEAR ENERGY INDUSTRY PERSPECTIVE ON POSSIBLE ICRP RECOMMENDATIONS ON RADIOLOGICAL ENVIRONMENT PROTECTION

Ralph. L. Andersen

CHP, Nuclear Energy Institute, Washington DC, USA

In the U.S., nuclear energy provides 20% of the nation's electricity. Of currently available energy sources, nuclear energy is among those with the least impact on the environment, especially in terms of unit energy produced. For example, nuclear plants do not emit gases potentially harmful to the environment – including those that have been associated with ground-level ozone formation, smog, acid rain and global warming. And the due to the relatively small area of land use and environmentally benign aspects of plant operations, nuclear sites preserve land and provide excellent habitat where diverse species of plants and animals, including a number of endangered species, live and thrive.

Nuclear energy is the lowest cost source of base load electrical generation in the U.S. Moreover, unlike many other forms of generation, the costs of preventing environmental degradation or pollution from nuclear electricity are internalised in the price to the consumer.

Nuclear power plants produce relatively small volumes of waste by-products, including used nuclear fuel and low-level radioactive waste. U.S. policy is to emplace and isolate used nuclear fuel in a deep geologic repository. Low-level radioactive waste products are contained for transport to licensed shallow land disposal facilities.

Radioactive material in liquid and gaseous effluents is maintained as low as reasonably achievable (ALARA), and in fact, is demonstrated to be in the range of $1/10,000^{th}$ to $1/100^{th}$ of federal radiation safety limits that are based on ICRP recommendations. Each plant collects and analyzes hundreds of environmental samples each year, including biological and non-biological media, to validate the effectiveness of radiological effluent control programs. Current experience with decommissioning of sites, although limited, indicates that residual levels of radioactive material following decommissioning are well below applicable federal radiation safety limits (also based on ICRP recommendations), and, due to the relatively short half-lives involved, will decay to levels indistinguishable from natural radiation background in several decades.

Although ICRP recommendations have been focused on radiological protection of humans, the ICRP has stated its belief that "the standard of environmental control needed to protect man to the degree currently thought desirable will ensure that other species are not put at risk." That belief has not been strictly validated by science, which has given rise to questions of whether a specific framework for radiological protection of non-human species and biota is warranted. The ICRP has formed a task group charged with "developing a protection policy and establishing a framework of environmental protection based on ethical-philosophical principles."

The nuclear energy industry's perspective on this ICRP activity is shaped in several ways – as an operator, we carry out a primary responsibility for protecting human health and safety and the environment; as a licensee, we are responsible for complying with government regulations; and as an energy producer, we are responsible for the safe, reliable, and economic generation of electricity for consumers.

The industry's interest in this ICRP activity is to help promote an outcome that is clear in its basis and objectives as they apply to protection of the environment, flexible in regard to how it might be applied to a very wide range of current and future regulated activities, and practical and cost-effective in terms of how it could be implemented and maintained.

The OECD/NEA Committee on Radiation Protection and Public Health proposes to conduct, in collaboration with the ICRP, 3 meetings to interact on this activity. We appreciate the opportunity to participate. In our own effort to understand and assess progress in this ICRP activity, we will seek answers to the following 3 questions at each stage of the process:

- What is the problem to be solved?

- How will the approach being considered solve the problem?

- How will the approach improve overall protection of the environment?

Our challenge to the ICRP is to frame responses to such questions on the basis of scientific knowledge and understanding, as well as ethical-philosophical principles. This is more in keeping with the acknowledged expertise of the ICRP. We recommend that the ICRP link the proposed framework that results from the current activity to public policy development and decision-making processes, and to avoid pre-empting such processes by the nature of the proposed ICRP framework. This would seem appropriate in light of the current state of the relevant science and the evolutionary nature of this ICRP activity. Finally, and most importantly, we encourage the ICRP to studiously avoid tunnel vision, e.g., by focusing too narrowly on "radiological" environmental protection. This effort should maintain perspective at all times on overall preservation of the environment in which we live and are a part. In short, we ask that the ICRP avoid "missing the forest for the trees."

PROBLEMS IN DEVELOPING A RATIONAL APPROACH
TO RADIOLOGICAL PROTECTION OF THE ENVIRONMENT
FROM A REGULATORY VIEWPOINT

Enrico Sgrilli and Giusseppi Tarroni
ANPA (National Agency for the Protection of the Environment),
ENEA (National Agency for New Technologies, Energy and the Environment)

Introduction

For a century science and technology have been concerned with the study of atomic and nuclear phenomena as well as their application for uses beneficial to mankind, from the production of electricity by nuclear reactors to a wide ranging array of uses of radiation in medicine, in industry and research.

As progress was being made in the application of radiation and of atomic and nuclear phenomena their effects on human health have also been extensively studied as well as ways and means to protect man from such effects. A wealth of scientific information has been gathered in time on the harmful effects of radiation on man, of which, let it suffice here to recall, the authoritative and comprehensive reports by the United Nations Scientific Committee on Sources and Effects of Atomic Radiation (UNSCEAR) and by the United States National Academy of Sciences (BEIR).

It is our good fortune that the wealth of scientific information available on the effects of radiation on man has admirably been organised and synthesised by ICRP into a coherent structure, both from the view point of creating quantities providing us with a way of "measuring" risk and harm and of proposing a rational system of protection that while allowing society to benefit from uses of radiation offers the framework and the conceptual tools needed to give adequate protection to man from its harmful effects.

The aim of this paper is to outline problems arising when trying to draw an obvious parallel between what is already extant for the radiation protection of man and the environment and what might further be thought feasible for the environment. For this purpose a brief summary will be made of the salient characteristics of the present radiation protection system, as recommended by ICRP and accepted *inter alia* in the IAEA Basic Safety Standards and European directives, estimates of radiation effects on biota and trends in environmental protection will be briefly reviewed, as well as the main challenges to meet.

Estimates of radiation risk for humans: a brief review

The assessment of risk obviously is an essential presupposition in the rational and efficacious management of any kind of risk. Radiation protection professionals are so accustomed to use, and to think in terms of, radiation protection quantities and concepts recommended by ICRP that we perhaps are a little spoiled and take these advanced and sophisticated tools for granted. It ought always to be borne in mind that the present system has its foundations on the evaluation of scientific studies that have been made for nearly a century on the effects of ionising radiation on man and on their interpretation by UNSCEAR and BEIR reports and ICRP Publications.

Indeed, crucial in our present knowledge are the estimates of radiological risk made over more than 50 years on the basis of laboratory and epidemiological evidence, notably the comprehensive scientific evaluation by, *inter alia*, UNSCEAR and BEIR of the results of the Life Span Study on the cohorts of Japanese Atomic Bomb survivors. It is common knowledge that at the end of the eighties such studies showed that the projected estimates of attributable cancer death probability had to be revised for various reasons, notably because of an increase in the excess solid cancers observed and of the new DS86 dosimetry; also, an important factor was that, with a view to obtaining an estimate of the lifetime mortality risk from exposure to an acute dose of low LET radiation, a multiplicative risk projection model was found to fit the then available mortality data better than the additive risk projection model in use up to that time.

The 1988 UNSCEAR report[1] gave an estimate of $7 \div 11 \ 10^{-2}$ as the lifetime probability of fatal cancer following an acute whole body dose of 1 Gy of low LET radiation; the first estimate referred to a total Japanese population using a multiplicative projection model and age-averaged coefficients and the second estimate using age-specific coefficients.

The 1990 BEIR V report[2] gave an estimate of $0.79 \ 10^{-2}$ for a whole body exposure to 0.1 Sv using a multiplicative projection model allowing for a diminishing probability with time since exposure; nonetheless, if account is taken of the leukaemia contribution for high dose and dose rate, the BEIR V estimate can be given as $8.85 \cdot 10^{-2} \ \mathrm{Sv}^{-1}$, in remarkably good accordance with the 1988 UNSCEAR estimate.

A new UNSCEAR report was published in the year 2000 (UNSCEAR 2000).[3] Taking account of a follow up of mortality in the Life Span Study of Japanese Atomic Bomb survivors the 2000 UNSCEAR report has confirmed the above estimate of radiation induced cancer risk. UNSCEAR 2000 has adopted a time constant relative risk model for solid cancers, the so called "age at exposure" model, according to which relative risk varies with age at exposure and sex but is constant with time since exposure, which is the same approach used in UNSCEAR 1994.[4] Results of estimates have also been calculated in UNSCEAR 2000 using the "attained-age" model, under which relative risk varies with age and sex but decreases with time since exposure. UNSCEAR 2000 has suggested a linear quadratic dose response model for leukaemia, a linear dose response model for solid

1. UNSCEAR, Sources, Effects and Risks of Ionizing Radiation, United Nations Scientific Committee on the Effects of Atomic Radiation, 1988 Report to the General Assembly, with annexes, United Nations, New York, 1988.

2. UNSCEAR, Sources and Effects of Ionizing Radiation, United Nations Scientific Committee on the Effects of Atomic Radiation, UNSCEAR 2000 Report to the General Assembly, with Scientific Annexes, Volume II: Effects, United Nations, New York, 2000.

3. NAS, Health Effects of Exposure to Low Levels of Ionizing Radiation, BEIR V Report, National Academy of Sciences, National Academy Press, Washington DC, 1990.

4. UNSCEAR, Sources, Effects and Risks of Ionizing Radiation, United Nations Scientific Committee on the Effects of Atomic Radiation, 1994 Report to the General Assembly, with annexes, United Nations, New York, 1994.

cancers; estimates for leukaemia have been made in the UNSCEAR 2000 report using an absolute risk model under which risk varies by age at exposure and time since exposure.

For all solid cancers combined and for an acute exposure of a Japanese population of both sexes to 1 Sv of low LET radiation, UNSCEAR 2000 has given an estimate of $11 \cdot 10^{-2}$ Sv^{-1}. The report has given an estimate of $1 \cdot 10^{-2}$ Sv^{-1} for leukaemia after an acute exposure to 1 Sv of low LET radiation.

Thus, risk projection models that have been in use over the last 12 years can be considered to give state of the art estimates of radiation induced cancer mortality, even though results may somewhat vary depending on the specific model; another factor to take account of is time as more results from the Life Span Study and other studies will be adding to our knowledge.

However, even though risk estimates of radiation induced cancer mortality from high level irradiation appear to be robust over the years, it should be kept in mind that the epidemiological evidence available is limited to high dose and dose rate exposures; no firm conclusion can be drawn yet as to the much sought after form of the relationship between dose and effects at low doses and dose rates or, for that matter, to the existence of a threshold. In this context it is interesting to mention that a study quoted in Annex I of the UNSCEAR 2000 Report has suggested a statistically significant increasing trend in mortality risks over the range up to 50 mSv for all solid cancers but the interpretation of the results is not straightforward.

Again, it is our good fortune that this wealth of scientific studies on deleterious effects has been interpreted and incorporated over the years by ICRP into a rational and coherent structure for the use of regulators and radiation protection professionals. On the basis of the scientific evidence available ICRP has defined an array of concepts and quantities enabling radiation protection professionals to confidently make assessments on radiation risk.[5,6]

We are at present able to make a science based distinction between effects of exposure which may arise in the individual affected (somatic effects) or in his offspring (genetic effects). Moreover, depending on the amount and the rate of ionising radiation received by an individual we can make a distinction between clinically observable effects arising above certain thresholds of exposure (deterministic effects) and those effects which only have a probability of happening (stochastic effects). What matters even more is that we have rather precise ideas of the amount of radiation exposure needed to cause deterministic effects and we are able to make estimates on the probability of stochastic effects from a conservative point of view (the so called Linear No Threshold Hypothesis).

An outline of the ICRP system

In the 1990 Recommendations[7] ICRP considered it appropriate to apply a dose and dose rate effectiveness factor (DDREF) of 2 to the "average" of the then available estimates of radiation risk, considering that the probability of effects at low doses and dose rates should be lower than at high

5. ICRP, Recommendations of the International Commission on Radiological Protection, ICRP Publication 26, Pergamon Press, 1977.

6. ICRP, 1990 Recommendations of the International Commission on Radiological Protection, ICRP Publication 60, Pergamon Press, 1991.

7. ICRP, 1990 Recommendations of the International Commission on Radiological Protection, ICRP Publication 60, Pergamon Press, 1991.

doses and dose rates; thus a nominal fatal cancer probability of $5 \cdot 10^{-2}$ Sv^{-1} was obtained for a population of all ages and both sexes, the nominal fatal cancer probability for a working population aged 20÷64 being given as $4 \cdot 10^{-2}$ Sv^{-1}. In this context, dose limits of 100 mSv in 5 years for workers and 1 mSv per year for the public were, *inter alia*, recommended in Publication 60 by ICRP.

Starting from absorbed dose, i.e. the amount of energy absorbed in a unit mass of a tissue or organ, which is a measurable quantity, and considering that the probability of stochastic effects depends on the type and energy of radiation causing the dose absorbed in the body or in particular tissues, ICRP has defined a radiation protection quantity, equivalent dose, formed by weighting the average dose absorbed in the tissue or organ of interest by *ad hoc* radiation weighting factors.

All other things being equal, the probability of stochastic effects is considered to depend on the organ or tissue irradiated, and ICRP has defined a further quantity, effective dose, derived from weighting equivalent doses in tissues or organs by suitable weighting factors, w_T, which make for an aggregate distribution of detriment in organs: effective dose is thought likely to correlate well with the total of stochastic effects. It is worth mentioning that the tissue weighting factors w_T recommended in ICRP Publication 60 appear to correlate well with those deductible from epidemiological data in the UNSCEAR 2000 report.

It is common knowledge that the ICRP recommended radiation protection framework "is intended to prevent the occurrence of deterministic effects, by keeping doses below the relevant thresholds, and to ensure that all reasonable steps are taken to reduce the induction of stochastic effects". The Commission has defined in Publication 60 a concept of detriment comprising 4 components, with a view to representing both the probability of occurrence of a harmful health effect and a judgement of the severity of that effect, taking account of the probability of attributable fatal cancer, the weighted probability of attributable non fatal cancer and severe hereditary effects and the expected length of life lost.

It is also widely known that the present radiation protection system is based on a distinction between practices and intervention; for practices are meant those programmed operations with sources under control which increase exposure to ionising radiation while those human actions with a view to diminishing exposure are taken into consideration under the concept of intervention, let it be either intervention in the context of an emergency resulting from an accident or intervention in situations leading to lasting exposure such as the after effects of radiological emergencies or of past practices.

ICRP has recommended three basic principles governing the protection system for practices, lately in ICRP Publication 60, which are justification of practices, optimisation of protection and individual dose limits. In short, the justification principle states that a practice can be adopted, that is, its inception is "justified" only if it produces more benefit to the exposed individuals or to society than the radiation detriment it causes. After justification has been established for a practice, application of the principle of optimisation of protection is the guiding criterion in deciding the optimum level of radiation protection to be applied to a specific source within a practice, taking account of economic and social considerations, in order to make an efficient use of economic resources available. As the application of the optimisation principle may not suffice to ensure adequate protection for all individuals affected by exposure to ionising radiation, the principle of dose limitation for practices has also been recommended by ICRP together with numerical limits which reflect the Commission's views on the border between unacceptable and tolerable exposures.

Similar, though differently worded, principles of justification and optimisation apply to intervention, apart from dose limits, which are not applicable.

In this venue there is no room to dwell at length on other characteristics of sophistication of the radiation protection system recommended by ICRP, let it suffice to remind us all of the advanced features reached in the ICRP models, e.g., those recommended in order to assess effective doses from internal exposure by nearly 800 radionuclides for various ages of the individuals concerned.

It must be emphasised that the current radiation protection philosophy resulting from ICRP thinking is embodied in the recommendations of international organisations as IAEA and NEA as well as, *inter alia*, in the regulatory system laid down in the European directives, notably in directive 96/29/Euratom[8] establishing Basic Safety Standards valid for all Member States of the European Union, which have a legal duty under the Euratom Treaty to transpose Euratom directives into their national legislation on radiation protection. The process of transposal into national legislation of the 1996 Euratom directive mentioned above has already taken place in Italy and other Member States.

Although there is room to make further progress in the present radiation protection system the authors feel it can be said that the system has reached levels of advancement and sophistication perhaps with no comparison with other risk assessment frameworks. Indeed, the levels of sophistication reached are such that the current ICRP recommendations are even criticised by some who argue that the system it is too complex and difficult to apply; the authors feel, though, that the ICRP system deserves praise for being both rational and well structured, complexity being inherent in the sophistication level itself.

Some positions on environmental radiation protection

As regards protection of the environment, in radiation protection philosophy and practice the tenet has, broadly, been for a long time that if man is adequately protected then species other than man are protected as well. This posture is reflected, *inter alia*, in the Recommendations of 1977 and 1990 by ICRP. In the 1977 Recommendations[9] ICRP stated that "Although the principal objective of radiation protection is the achievement and maintenance of appropriately safe conditions for activities involving human exposure, the level of safety required for the protection of human individuals is thought likely to be adequate to protect other species, although not necessarily individual members of those species. Therefore the Commission believes that if man is adequately protected then other living things are also likely to be sufficiently protected".

On the other hand, the current ICRP posture as embodied in paragraph 16 of ICRP Publication 60 of 1990[10] is that "The Commission believes that the standards of environmental control needed to protect man to the degree currently thought desirable will ensure that other species are not put at risk. Occasionally, individual members of non-human species might be harmed, but not to the extent of endangering whole species or of creating imbalances between species".

The ICRP position has been the target of criticism by some as it was thought to be excessively man centred even though some criticisms might be considered to be somewhat unfair,

---

8. Council Directive 96/29/Euratom of 13 May 1996 laying down basic safety standards for the protection of the health of workers and the general public against the dangers arising from ionising radiation, Official Journal of the European Communities, L 159, Volume 39, 29 June 1996.

9. ICRP, Recommendations of the International Commission on Radiological Protection, ICRP Publication 26, Pergamon Press, 1977.

10. ICRP, 1990 Recommendations of the International Commission on Radiological Protection, ICRP Publication 60, Pergamon Press, 1991.

given that the assumption has never been convincingly disproved except for very specific instances that will be mentioned below. Moreover, it must be kept in mind that at the moment there appears to be no easy solution to the problem of developing a rational and unified framework to satisfy the need to protect both man and other forms of life from ionising radiation.

Some segments of the scientific community viewed the ICRP approach with perplexity because ICRP statements might not be applicable to all situations, e.g. where humans or pathways to man are absent or restricted but biota have access, where unique exposure pathways exist or to practices such as deep sea dumping, which has been discontinued.

For some time the problem of protecting the environment from the effects of ionising radiation has been the subject of regulatory concern both by some national regulatory agencies and by supranational bodies dealing with radiation protection. Some statements to this effect by IAEA and the European Union will be quoted here.

As far as radioactive waste is concerned, IAEA[11] has established a principle (Principle 2) on the protection of the environment relating to radioactive waste management "Radioactive waste shall be managed in such a way as to provide an acceptable level of protection of the environment."; besides, for protection beyond national borders Principle 3 states "Radioactive waste shall be managed in such a way as to assure that possible effects on human health and the environment beyond national borders will be taken into account".

As regards the European Union, the requirement of "achieving and maintaining an optimal level of protection of the environment and the population" has been laid down, in the context of protection of the public, as a responsibility of undertakings intending to carry out a practice in article 47(a) of Title VIII ("Radiation protection of the population in normal circumstances") of directive 96/29/Euratom.[12]

There is, however, no comprehensive internationally agreed upon framework for radiological protection of the environment; the need for international consensus with a view to elaborating a well thought-out policy in this matter is certainly there and the efforts to this end by ICRP and other bodies such as the European Commission, IAEA and NEA must certainly be welcomed.

The ambition would obviously be to incorporate concepts and principles used in environmental protection into the existing framework for radiation protection of man with a view to establishing a coherent and integrated system valid for both radiation protection of man and of the environment. A brief review will be made of the main problems and it must be acknowledged that the task at hand appears by no means easy.

Sustainable development and the precautionary principle

The sustainable development principle is the first that should be considered for formal inclusion into the radiation protection framework, meaning for sustainable development "a development that meets the needs of the present without compromising the ability of future

---

11. IAEA, The Principles of Radioactive Waste Management, Safety Fundamentals, Safety Series no. 111-F, IAEA, Vienna, 1995.

12. Council Directive 96/29/Euratom of 13 May 1996 laying down basic safety standards for the protection of the health of workers and the general public against the dangers arising from ionising radiation, Official Journal of the European Communities, L 159, Volume 39, 29 June 1996.

generations to meet their own needs" as per the definition reported in the NEA Report[13] of 2000 on Nuclear Energy in a Sustainable Development Perspective. In the words of the NEA Report "Sustainable development essentially tells us that all our activities have long-term implications, and they should all be managed with an eye to the future" and, as such, the three dimensions of sustainable development, that is, economy, the environment and social considerations do not appear to be a wholly new way of thinking as far as radiation protection is concerned.

Indeed, radiation protection is a science accustomed to thinking in terms of the future; for a long time regulators and radiation protection professionals have had to meet the conceptual challenge of trying to assess future consequences, sometimes far into the future, of present actions and situations, as is the case e.g. for the management of long living radioactive wastes.

Putting radiation protection philosophy and practice formally in tune with a sustainable development perspective is an effort that should require consideration with a view to introducing possible adjustments to existing principles of justification, optimisation and, possibly, dose limitation.

In this context, it must also be mentioned that article 6 of the European Community Treaty establishes that environmental protection requirements must be integrated into the definition and the implementation of Community policies and activities concerning health, safety, environmental protection and consumer protection, in particular with a view to promoting sustainable development.

Closely linked with the principle of sustainable development is the precautionary principle, which has been introduced in various international documents. The precautionary approach was first introduced into the World Charter for Nature (1982), stated in "The Rio Declaration on the Environment and Development" (1992) and later adopted in the same year by the European Union Maastricht Treaty.

The precautionary approach, as stated in "The Rio Declaration on the Environment and Development" (Principles 15), establishes that: "In order to protect the environment, the precautionary approach shall be widely applied by States according to their capabilities. Where there are threats of serious or irreversible damage, lack of full scientific certainty shall not be used as a reason for postponing cost-effective measures to prevent environmental degradation". In other words, in order to correctly implement the principle it is necessary to collect enough scientific information allowing the identification of effects, even if not fully demonstrated, and to establish criteria and methodology flexible enough to be adapted to scientific progress.

From a European regulatory standpoint, the precautionary principle has become a legal rule for the protection of the environment in the European Union since 1992 when it was legislated into the European Community Treaty. Article 174 of the Treaty states specifically in paragraph 2 that "Community policy on the environment shall aim at a high level of protection ... It shall be based on the precautionary principle and on the principles that preventive action should be taken, that environmental damage should as a priority be rectified at the source..."; paragraph 3 of article 174 goes on stating that in preparing its policy on the environment the Community shall take account of available scientific and technical data, as well as potential benefits and costs of action or lack of action.

---

13. NEA, Nuclear Energy in a Sustainable Development Perspective, OECD Nuclear Energy Agency, Paris, 2000.

Basically, the precautionary principle is considered by the European Commission[14] a risk analysis tool; the Commission has indicated that recourse to the principle presupposes two conditions. The first one being the identification of possible negative effects and the second is the presence of scientific evaluations which are, however, insufficient, inconclusive or imprecise to determine the risk in question with sufficient certainty, e.g. in those cases where cause-effect relationships are suspected but have not been demonstrated.

The European Commission has warned against confusion between a prudential approach and the precautionary principle, considering that a prudential approach is, broadly, part of the scientific opinions rendered by risk evaluators whilst the principle is part of risk management and, as such, its application is ultimately a matter for decision makers. The Commission has also clarified that application of the precautionary principle may well result in a decision to take no action if judgement on scientific data, potential benefits and costs indicates on balance that no action is the best choice, i.e. "The decision to do nothing is a response in its own right" and again "The appropriate response in a given situation is thus the result of an eminently political decision, a function of the risk level that is 'acceptable' to the society on which the risk is imposed".

Like the principle of sustainable development, the precautionary principle does not appear alien to radiation protection thinking. It is common knowledge that no firm scientific evidence exists at the moment for effects on man of exposure to low level ionising radiation, yet the framework of radiation protection addresses the problem of stochastic effects assuming a non zero probability for such effects and adopting the Linear No Threshold hypothesis on the basis of scientific considerations on the mechanism of cancer induction.

The challenge of a formal introduction of the principle into the existing radiation protection framework might thus be considered.

A short review of radiation effects on biota

Nor do difficulties end here; with a view to integrating environmental radiation protection into the existing system for humans other challenges are perhaps more complex.

When dealing with protection of the environment from adverse effects of ionising radiation it is obviously necessary to have a clear understanding of such effects on other forms of life. To this end, the very laboratory research in radiobiology that has been and will be used with a view to enhancing our knowledge of deleterious effects on man will certainly contribute to progress in the information available as regards harmful effects on other life forms.

Moreover, there exist several studies in the field of environmental protection from the effects of ionising radiation, and among such documents it is worthwhile mentioning for their regulatory relevance the IAEA reports in 1988 and in 1992 respectively on the effects of deep sea radioactive waste disposal on living marine resources[15] and on plants and animals,[16] a comprehensive review of the existing literature on this subject was made in 1996 by an authoritative body such as UNSCEAR.[17]

---

14. Commission of the European Communities, Communication from the Commission on the precautionary principle, COM(2000), Brussels, 2.2.2000.

15. IAEA, Assessing the Impact of Deep Sea Disposal of Low level Radioactive Waste on Living Marine Resources, Technical Reports Series no. 288, IAEA, Vienna, 1988.

The 1988 IAEA report[18] on deep sea disposal of low level radioactive waste, a practice that has been discontinued, concluded that deep sea biota were likely to incur effects decreasing in severity with decreasing doses and three types of situations were identified. The first situation would involve extensive mortality in areas where dose rates are greater than 10 mSv/h although it was felt unlikely that entire populations would be destroyed owing to the usually wide distribution of deep sea populations. The second situation concerns dose rates of about 1 mSv/h above which effects on reproduction, development and genetic integrity would be detectable in sensitive organisms. The third situation concerns dose rates less than 1 mSv/h, but greater than background, where genetic changes resulting in somatic effects might occur but it was felt that such somatic effects would be eliminated by natural selection with little or no effect at the population level.

The objective of the 1992 IAEA report[19] on effects of radiation on plants and animals was to ascertain whether compliance with current radiological protection standards for the population would also imply, as held by ICRP, adequate protection for such non human life forms; thus, the review and evaluation of existing literature made by IAEA was mainly centred on effects on plants and animals exposed to low levels of ionising radiation, e.g. deriving from routine discharges of radioactive effluents, although acute effects were also taken into consideration.

For effects at the population level for non human species the 1992 IAEA report has acknowledged that the possibility of harmful effects at the individual level could be masked in cases of effects not frequent enough to be revealed at the population level.

Moreover, the 1992 IAEA report has emphasised the need to address the problem of taking account of indirect response to ionising radiation; that is, if several species receive doses in a biotic community, it may well happen that only a species more sensitive to radiation shows effects but other species may suffer adverse consequences only owing to their dependence on the more sensitive one. The example was made in the report of irradiation at a dose rate of 0.5 Gy/d of species within a pine forest, where pines would experience severe mortality whilst other species might not be directly affected; even so, perturbations, not necessarily negative, caused by irradiation might indirectly happen in populations of such species.

The 1992 IAEA report considered that "chronic dose rates of $1 \text{ mGy} \cdot \text{d}^{-1}$ or less to even the more radiosensitive species in terrestrial ecosystems are unlikely to cause measurable detrimental effects in populations" and concluded "There is no convincing evidence from the scientific literature that chronic radiation dose rates below $1 \text{ mGy} \cdot \text{d}^{-1}$ will harm animal or plant populations."; besides, the report considered that adequate protection for a population in the aquatic environment would be provided by limiting chronic dose rates to 10 mGy/d to the maximally exposed individuals in population.

16. IAEA, Effects of Ionising Radiation on Plants and Animals at Levels implied by current Radiation Protection Standards, Technical Reports Series no. 332, IAEA, Vienna, 1992.

17. UNSCEAR, Effects of Radiation on the Environment, Annex to Sources and Effects of Ionising Radiation, Scientific Committee on the Effects of Atomic Radiation, United Nations, New York, 1996.

18. IAEA, Assessing the Impact of Deep Sea Disposal of Low level Radioactive Waste on Living Marine Resources, Technical Reports Series no. 288, IAEA, Vienna, 1988.

19. IAEA, Effects of Ionising Radiation on Plants and Animals at Levels implied by current Radiation Protection Standards, Technical Reports Series no. 332, IAEA, Vienna, 1992.

The dose calculations to non human life forms were considered by the IAEA report[20] as being conservative by 1÷2 orders of magnitude, thus guaranteeing adequate safety margins in the doses actually incurred to plants and animals if radiation protection standards for the public are complied with. The report cautioned, however, that site specific analyses might still be required in some situations such as prolonged exposures to man of nearly 1 mSv/y together with, e.g., presence of rare or endangered species.

The 1992 IAEA report has also addressed the problem of an appropriate definition for the concept of population; the report states that defining a population entirely depends on the specific case under consideration as well as on the space and time scale of interest; a definition for this concept is proposed as useful in the following terms "A population is a biological unit for study, with a number of varying statistics (e.g. number, density, birth rate, death rate, sex ratio, age distribution), and which derives a biological meaning from the fact that some direct or indirect interactions among its members are more important than those between its members and members of other populations".

The results of the 1992 IAEA report were endorsed in a workshop[21] sponsored in 1995 by the US Department of Energy; participants in the workshop were in agreement that the degree of protection given to man generally guarantees protection of non human life forms "except when (1) human access is restricted but access by biota is not restricted, (2) unique exposure pathways exist, (3) rare or endangered species are present, or (4) other stresses are significant."

The objective of the Annex to the 1996 UNSCEAR report[22] has been to review the information available on radiation exposures from natural radiation background or radioactive releases, either planned or accidental, as well as responses to acute and chronic irradiation of plants and animals, both as individuals and as populations. Effects on ecosystems arising from accidents at the nuclear materials production complex of Mayak near Kyshtym in 1977 and at Chernobyl in 1986 have specifically been reviewed.

In the accident at Mayak 74 PBq of fission products were released as aerosols, 95% with half lives of one year or less, and 15 000 km^2 of territory were contaminated by ^{90}Sr at a concentration greater than 3.7 kBq m^{-2}. The largest part of the irradiation was delivered within the first year when radionuclide decay was about 66%, with β radiation being three times larger than γ; as a consequence, the distribution of dose rate in space and time was regulated by deposition and subsequently by environmental processes.

The main part of the exposure happened in autumn and winter during the metabolic resting period of plants and animals; this fact determined an apparent radiation resistance that conversely implied inhibition of repair mechanisms. Thus, when effects were observed in spring they were more related with accumulated dose than with dose rate, which is typical of chronic exposure. Major damage affected pines, the middle and lower parts of the canopy being more damaged as contamination in the upper canopy was cleared by wind and rain; pines were found to die at 15÷20 Gy

20. IAEA, Effects of Ionising Radiation on Plants and Animals at Levels implied by current Radiation Protection Standards, Technical Reports Series no. 332, IAEA, Vienna, 1992.

21. L. W. Barnthouse, Effects of Ionising Radiation on Terrestrial Plants and Animals,: a Workshop Report prepared for the US Department of Energy, Oak Ridge National Laboratory, Environmental Science Division, Publication no. 4494, ORNL/TM-1341, Oak Ridge, Tennessee, US, December 1995.

22. UNSCEAR, Effects of Radiation on the Environment, Annex to Sources and Effects of Ionising Radiation, Scientific Committee on the Effects of Atomic Radiation, United Nations, New York, 1996.

while birch trees at doses less than 200 Gy. Among sublethal effects a shift in development timing was observed.

The most sensitive herbaceous species were those in which dormant buds were located at or near the soil surface, such species were found to disappear at contamination of $18 \div 26$ MBq m^{-2}. Long term effects were observed on *Chloral vulgaris*, a soil alga, which was found to acquire a stabilised radiation resistance and to decrease in viability, apparently owing to radiation induced genetic mutations.

Among invertebrate populations, those inhabiting the birch forest litter or underlying surface, and saprophages in particular, where the most severely affected due to sedentary lifestyles, while mobile predators were less affected. In areas where ^{90}Sr contamination was $165 \div 340$ MBq m^{-2}, mesofauna was reduced after 11 years to less than 50%. Different species of invertebrates received different radiation exposures even with radionuclide deposition being equal because of their specific behaviour and habitat; moreover, radiation doses being equal a range in radiation responses was observed owing to interspecies and age related differences in radiosensitivity. Animals were more damaged if pre-adult stages of life were spent in the litter and surface soil.

Populations of small rodents were studied for more than 40 generations. Among the effects reported there were increased death rate, declining in reproductive performance, changes of behaviour, chromosomal damage, increased resistance to stress and to radiation, adaptation. On the other hand, no effect on reproductive performance and genetic damage of fish was observed below $400 \div 1,200$ µGy/h.

In the accident at Chernobyl there was a total radioactive release of about 2 EBq, noble gases being excluded. The accident occurred in April, when plants and animals were at their most sensitive. About 80% of the exposure was delivered within 3 months, 95% being due to β radiation.

Among plants, spruce trees were observed to be more sensitive than pine trees. A marked reduction was observed in 1986-1987 in the number of species in the litter microarthropod community of the forest while larger invertebrates appear to have been less affected.

Dose to small rodents in the acute phase might have reached lethality levels (880 Gy) and some effects have been observed at the individual level; no evidence of teratogenic effects has been found in domestic animals outside the 30 km exclusion zone.

In this context, a number of remarks appear in order. Whilst levels of radioactivity originating from controlled radioactive releases are usually too low to induce effects observable in the different constituents of an ecosystem, the unfortunate occurrence of severe accidents gave us the opportunity to observe severe acute damage and long term effects in individual organisms and populations. This made it also possible to gain experience on sensitive species and on the cascade of consequences induced by the first impact of acute radioactivity releases: the information could constitute a basis to establish markers of exposure and of effects.

However, a number of inherent limitations must also be kept in mind. Any accident is unique due to different modalities of release, dispersal, deposition, hydrogeological conditions; in an accident the main concern is, understandably, to evaluate human risk and the more severe is an accident the more limited are resources to evaluate risk to the environment.

As the relationship between dose rate and effects on wild organisms is dependent on the space and time variation in radionuclide concentration, assessment of doses is necessarily imprecise, being based on retrospective measurements of long lived radionuclides. Also, chemistry and radiation characteristics of radionuclides influence their behaviour while geometry characteristics and distribution of species respectively affect dosimetry and sensitivity. The three stages after release may be distinguished in three phases in relation to effects:

- an acute phase, due to the action of short lived radionuclides that provoke immediate or almost immediate biological effects;

- an intermediate phase, characterised by lower doses and possible redistribution of long lived radionuclides; in the case where high dose rates persist, this could prevent recovery from previous damage;

- a final, long-term phase, characterised by recovery or adaptation if the previous damage was not too severe.

Also, from the 1996 UNSCEAR report a number of lessons can be learnt:

- data on exposure from natural background are limited to a very restricted variety of organisms, indicative for aquatic environment;

- dose estimates derive from localised measurements and from models that assume an equilibrium state and do not take into account short term fluctuations in discharge rates, life cycle stages, changes in behaviour, seasonality;

- contribution from natural background is mainly due to α particles determining tissue specific dose rates;

- radiation exposure to some individuals in wild populations can reach 100 µGy h^{-1}, when dosimeters were used *in vivo* dose rates estimates were confirmed;

- following severe accidents damage has been observed in individual organisms and populations and long-term effects can develop;

- the response of plants and animals to chronic radiation exposure up to a maximum absorbed dose rate of 1 mGy h^{-1} can provide a basis for assessing the environmental impact of controlled radioactive waste release. For accident situations, when initial dose rates are high enough to allow accumulation of lethal doses, data are needed all the way to the upper ends (1,000 µGy h^{-1}).

As far as plants are concerned, the Annex has concluded that the effects of chronic irradiation were noted at dose rates of 1÷3 mGy/h in the most sensitive plant species and there were suggestions that chronic dose rates of less than 10 mGy/d would have slight effects in sensitive plants but "would be unlikely to have significant deleterious effects in the wider range of plants present in natural plant communities".

As far animals are concerned, the conclusions of the Annex have been that "For the most sensitive animal species, mammals, there is little indication that dose rates of 400 µGy·h^{-1} would seriously affect mortality in the population"; in respect of reproductive effects the same statement could be made for dose rates of 40÷100 µGy/h. The conclusion for aquatic organisms has been that maximum dose rates of 400 µGy·h^{-1} to a small proportion of the individuals, which implies a lower average dose rate to the remaining organisms, "would not have any detrimental effects at the population level".

The Annex has pointed out that available exposure data are limited to a very restricted variety of wild life forms and, amongst others, more information is needed on the time distribution of doses during the life cycle of interest, e.g. embryonic development. Another point made in the Annex is that assessment of doses needed to produce deleterious effects is fraught with difficulties owing to causes such as long term recovery and confounding factors. In general, species sensitivity has been found to depend on the stage of life at the moment of exposure, embryos and developing forms being more sensitive than adults.

From the view point of lethal effects, the Annex has reported that the sensitivity of living organisms varies over a wide range, with mammals being the most sensitive among animals and plants showing a sensitivity range generally overlapping that of animals. Lessons learnt from the Mayak and Chernobyl accidents have confirmed the role of sensitivity in that effects were found to be different among species.

Environmental radiation protection: what targets?

The above mentioned considerations point out, *inter alia*, a problem that ought to be clearly addressed.

The present system of radiation protection is centred upon the protection of man from deleterious effects of ionising radiation, where protection means, broadly, the avoidance of deterministic effects as well as keeping the probability of occurrence of stochastic effects in man and his offspring acceptably low: as far as radiation protection of the environment is concerned what should the targets of protection be?

Should we provide protection for animal and vegetal forms of life as species, or should we also aim at providing an adequate degree of protection for individual members of species?

It would seem that the concept of biodiversity also plays an important role in this context. The concept of biodiversity has been defined in the United Nations Convention on Biological Diversity signed at Rio in 1992 as "The variability among living organisms from all sources including, inter alia, terrestrial, marine, and other aquatic ecosystems and the ecological complexes of which they are part; this includes diversity within species, between species and of ecosystems". From a European regulatory standpoint it is worthwhile remarking that the European Union and all 18 Member States (Italy among them) of the European Environment Agency (EEA) are signatories to the Convention.

In a report[23] by the Institute of Terrestrial Ecology on behalf of the European Environment Agency on the subject of biodiversity, an estimate of the number of species alone was made as being between 5 and 30 million, the majority of them not having yet been described. The report has pointed out that the concept of biodiversity implies diversity between and within ecosystems and habitats, diversity of species, and genetic variation within individual species; thus, the concept of biodiversity goes far beyond the multiplicity of species and includes assemblies of life forms making up ecosystems and natural habitats, beside the variability of genes within species.

Clearly, judicious scientific synthesis is a must if the problem of protecting the environment is to be solved in a rational and efficient manner: the variety of types of fauna and flora is very considerable, indeed almost infinite for all practical purposes, such as to make it unrealistic or perhaps downright impossible to develop adequate dose assessment models and to obtain the necessary data to

---

23. I. S. Anderson, C E Davies and D Moss, The UN Convention on Biological Diversity. Follow-up in EEA Member Countries 1996, Institute of Terrestrial Ecology, European Environment Agency, Copenhagen, 1997.

feed into the models for each and every species. In close analogy with existing methodology and concepts for the radiation protection of man two methods are possible and have been identified in a recent IAEA document[24] intended to stimulate discussion.

On one hand, the IAEA document has felt that recourse might be made to identifying reference types of fauna and flora and defining relevant dose models and necessary data. Another method would advocate the identification of critical species for a given environmental situation, that is, the species most sensitive to radiation effects in a given ecosystem, the idea obviously being that if the critical species is protected then all other species are too.

As in other scientific literature in this matter, the IAEA document has considered reproduction, that is, embryos and gametes, to be the most sensitive phase in living organisms and the recommendation is made that genetic damage should be kept under review even at dose rates lower than those causing significant changes in reproduction; this is because it appears that effects occurring at the population level caused by genetic changes are very complex, more than it would be expected.

In order to realise the ambition of achieving a logical and well structured system for radiation protection of the environment that should ideally be integrated into the existing ICRP recommended framework of radiological protection for man, the obvious method is drawing for inspiration on the well tried methodology for radiation protection of humans. To this end, certain mutually linked prerequisites can be identified from a technical standpoint.

Given the huge variety of species and the variability among them, the first obvious condition is the identification of reference/critical species and of the endpoints of interest (morbidity, mortality, fertility, fecundity, mutation rate etc.) in relation with exposure to radiation. Criteria for the choice of reference species will also have to be defined; proposals for this purpose[25,26] include those life forms likely to have the greatest potential for exposure owing to mechanisms of environmental transfer and to concentration factors of radionuclides; those organisms having a high radiosensitivity should be candidates for inclusion as well. In a broader perspective, two more criteria have been proposed,[27] i.e., including in reference species those organisms important to the "healthy" functioning of the community or of the ecosystem, as well as those organisms which are common.

On the other hand, the choice of reference organisms clearly requires a knowledge of dose-effects relationships for the species of interest; ideally, this would comprise effects deriving from low doses. Again, establishing a relationship between doses and effects for non human species requires a satisfactory estimate of the doses received with which effects are suitably to be correlated.

This requirement poses another problem: how to estimate doses to non human life forms in such a manner as to take account of effects. At present, doses to non human organisms are expressed as absorbed dose rates in grays per unit time but this does not seem to take account of the relative biological effectiveness of the different types of radiation which may be involved and of target organs

---

24. IAEA, Protection of the Environment from the effects of ionising radiation. A report for discussion, IAEA-Tecdoc-1091, IAEA, 1999, Vienna.

25. IAEA, Protection of the Environment from the effects of ionising radiation. A report for discussion, IAEA-Tecdoc-1091, IAEA, 1999, Vienna.

26. P. Strand *et al.*, Doses and Effects in Non-human Systems, Summary of the work of the action group of UIR, Per Strand, IUR 2000, available on the web site http://www.iur-uir.com/.

27. P. Strand *et al.*, Doses and Effects in Non-human Systems, Summary of the work of the action group of UIR, Per Strand, IUR 2000, available on the web site http://www.iur-uir.com/.

of interest. This is an area that might be explored with a view to establishing whether present scientific knowledge warrants the definition of a quantity similar to equivalent dose for all or for some of the species. This would require, amongst other things, adequate models for retention and deposition of radionuclides in biota of interest as well as judgement whether to forge and apply such models to all forms of life candidate to reference species or to the most complex forms only.

Final remarks

The authors feel that a long way in painstaking research on the environment is needed if we are to reach a degree of knowledge similar to the one we have now for man: it is to be pointed out that we have reached our present knowledge after more than a century since the first harmful effects of ionising radiation on man appeared and, notably, after fifty years of the Life Span Study on the radiation effects on the populations exposed at Hiroshima and Nagasaki.

Yet, after all this imposing amount of scientific efforts there is still room for considerable scientific progress in areas relevant to man's radiation protection. There is no certainty notably about the relationship between doses and effects at low doses and dose rates, as well as in other areas of interest such as possible developments in the matter of man's genetic susceptibility to cancer which may have to be kept under review, as the Commission stated in Publication 79[28]. Nor do we know whether and when we shall reach a satisfactory degree of knowledge on these and other difficult subjects.

It seems clear that a great deal of thought, drawing on available results of research, is needed in order to ascertain what the targets of protective actions should be and how to protect them. It seems appropriate to say that a substantial effort should be made with a view to reaching an efficacious scientific synthesis, in close analogy with what is current thinking and practice in radiation protection, e.g., as regards the solution used in Annex B of ICRP Publication 60 for national and sex differences. ICRP made a meritorious scientific effort of transfer and projection for five populations (Japan, the United States, Puerto Rico, the United Kingdom and China) of the data on relative probabilities of fatal cancer from the Japanese cohorts of survivors, averaging for males and females in order to have "a nominal 'world' population of all ages from which to derive the detriment".

Nor are difficulties limited to the aspects mentioned, important though they are, if the ambition is to realise a structured and integrated system of protection for man and other life forms: internationally agreed upon guidance on criteria and methodology should be forthcoming, in particular for those cases where conflicts may arise between the need to protect man and that to protect other species, given that the possibility of such situations cannot be ruled out *a priori*, notably in case of accidents.

Considering what approaches have been adopted for pollutants other than radiation is another aspect that requires thought. Should we try to harmonise all environmental aspects, radiological as well as conventional? The authors feel that the objective goes far beyond the problem of radiation protection of the environment because it concerns radiation protection with no qualifiers, the question being whether to strive at a framework comprising protection from ionising radiation as well as from other pollutants. Again, the crucible of the matter is: how should we "weigh" hazards of different nature?

---

28. ICRP, Genetic susceptibility to Cancer, ICRP Publication 79, Pergamon, 1999.

Conclusions

The traditional radiation protection view broadly summarised in the statement "if man is adequately protected then other living things are also likely to be sufficiently protected" (ICRP Publication 26) has been considered not to be applicable to all situations. A trend in the current international debate on an environmental radiation protection system shares the view that the environment has a value in itself and that protection of the environment is one of the means to protect man.

In recent times a considerable amount of efforts on the environment (publications, studies, projects and proposals for guidelines) has been produced by international agencies and researchers. The challenge is now to translate the above mentioned ongoing change of approach and the scientific results available into an integrated regulatory system for protection of both man and the environment.

The effects of ionising radiation on man have been extensively investigated for nearly a century, and in the light of these studies ongoing progress has been made in radiation protection of humans achieving a rational and well structured system where high levels of sophistication have been reached. Ecological risk assessment is a much more recent branch of scientific knowledge, fraught with remarkable difficulties, e.g. years will be needed, it is felt, to establish coherent approaches in order to assess radiation doses to biota.

In human risk assessment both target (man) and potential effects (cancer) are known, the latter to an adequate degree; on the contrary, in ecological risk assessment targets and types of effects have still to be established on an adequate scientific basis, as effects are thought to be different depending on the type of ecosystem: a judicious measure of scientific synthesis is clearly needed in this respect. The question is whether it is reasonable to wait until environmental knowledge equals what we know about radiation protection of man.

Principles relevant to environmental protection have been established at the regulatory level, notably the precautionary principle as well as e.g. sustainable development. The challenge is to realise an integrated protection system encompassing environmental principles into a unified framework.

The financial resources available for human and environmental protection from radiological risk are limited; it is therefore crucial to accurately and carefully choose objectives and plan interventions in order to avoid an unbalanced use of resources producing as a consequence a significant reduction in prevention.

Among other challenges to meet, coherent criteria have to be created and quantifiable markers to be selected. Adequate dosimetric quantities, models and significant markers of impact have also to be established on reference organisms (more sensitive species, species on the top of the alimentary chain or processes such as reproduction and decomposition?).

Should we consider as an objective to establish reference dose levels for equilibrium conditions and a trivial dose level as well? Can we extend to environmental protection the philosophy of dose limits set by ICRP for humans, or is it more correct to choose a limited number of "benchmark" dose levels for reference organisms and just monitor exceeding values? What about reference values for accidents? How can we manage the well known difficulties to directly measure biota radiation exposure and assess compliance?

We are also urged on by present needs, i.e. radioactive waste management, and international consensus is crucial with a view to developing common criteria and methodology for environmental radiation protection.

References

1. UNSCEAR, Sources, Effects and Risks of Ionising Radiation, United Nations Scientific Committee on the Effects of Atomic Radiation, 1988 Report to the General Assembly, with annexes, United Nations, New York, 1988.

2. UNSCEAR, Sources and Effects of Ionising Radiation, United Nations Scientific Committee on the Effects of Atomic Radiation, UNSCEAR 2000 Report to the General Assembly, with Scientific Annexes, Volume II: Effects, United Nations, New York, 2000.

3. NAS, Health Effects of Exposure to Low Levels of Ionising Radiation, BEIR V Report, National Academy of Sciences, National Academy Press, Washington DC, 1990.

4. UNSCEAR, Sources, Effects and Risks of Ionising Radiation, United Nations Scientific Committee on the Effects of Atomic Radiation, 1994 Report to the General Assembly, with annexes, United Nations, New York, 1994.

5. ICRP, Recommendations of the International Commission on Radiological Protection, ICRP Publication 26, Pergamon Press, 1977.

6. ICRP, 1990 Recommendations of the International Commission on Radiological Protection, ICRP Publication 60, Pergamon Press, 1991.

7. Council Directive 96/29/Euratom of 13 May 1996 laying down basic safety standards for the protection of the health of workers and the general public against the dangers arising from ionising radiation, Official Journal of the European Communities, L 159, Volume 39, 29 June 1996.

8. IAEA, The Principles of Radioactive Waste Management, Safety Fundamentals, Safety Series no. 111-F, IAEA, Vienna, 1995.

9. NEA, Nuclear Energy in a Sustainable Development Perspective, OECD Nuclear Energy Agency, Paris, 2000.

10. Commission of the European Communities, Communication from the Commission on the precautionary principle, COM(2000), Brussels, 2.2.2000.

11. IAEA, Assessing the Impact of Deep Sea Disposal of Low level Radioactive Waste on Living Marine Resources, Technical Reports Series no. 288, IAEA, Vienna, 1988.

12. IAEA, Effects of Ionising Radiation on Plants and Animals at Levels implied by current Radiation Protection Standards, Technical Reports Series no. 332, IAEA, Vienna, 1992.

13. UNSCEAR, Effects of Radiation on the Environment, Annex to Sources and Effects of Ionising Radiation, Scientific Committee on the Effects of Atomic Radiation, United Nations, New York, 1996.

14. L.W. Barnthouse, Effects of Ionising Radiation on Terrestrial Plants and Animals,: a Workshop Report prepared for the US Department of Energy, Oak Ridge National Laboratory, Environmental Science Division, Publication no. 4494, ORNL/TM-1341, Oak Ridge, Tennessee, US, December 1995.

15. I.S. Anderson, C.E. Davies and D. Moss, The UN Convention on Biological Diversity. Follow-up in EEA Member Countries 1996, Institute of Terrestrial Ecology, European Environment Agency, Copenhagen, 1997.

16. IAEA, Protection of the Environment from the effects of ionising radiation. A report for discussion, IAEA-Tecdoc-1091, IAEA, 1999, Vienna.

17. P. Strand *et al.*, Doses and Effects in Non-human Systems, Summary of the work of the action group of UIR, Per Strand, IUR 2000, available on the web site http://www.iur-uir.com/.

18. ICRP, Genetic susceptibility to Cancer, ICRP Publication 79, Pergamon, 1999.

PANEL DISCUSSION*

Question 1: What are the socio-political dynamics, beyond science, that will influence policy on radiological protection of the environment?

The panel compromised of experts representing views of the regulator, the operator, radiation protection and science. All panellists agreed that socio-political factors, beyond science, influenced policy.

Specific influences mentioned included:

- the growing interest in environmental issues in general, both at a national and international level (i.e., Rio);

- public concern about environmental and nuclear issues;

- the wish to explicitly demonstrate protection of the environment (even though the majority of respondents pointed out that, to date, radionuclide release from nuclear power had probably not caused significant ecological damage to non-human biota);

- a need for better comparison of environmental effects of radiation with other stressors and pollutants; and

- the requirement to meet commercial, economic and legal commitments (including liability, accountability, and commitments to employees).

Some other specific points are summarised as follows:

Other experience

At present, many nuclear sites are already subject to environmental laws and constraints covering any industry. Radionuclides are not the only pollutant released by such sites, and operations can influence the environment in a number of other ways (heat, construction). A number of people drew parallels with other industrial/societal risks, highlighting that the nuclear industry is not the only case where factors other than science influence policy.

Links with science

A number of respondents referred to relative influence of science and other factors on policy. Even though one could accept that science was not the only thing influencing policy, some people were worried that too little attention was paid to scientific knowledge. It was also pointed out that

---

* Kindly provided by Deborah Oughton.

there is a reflective influence between science, policy and socio-political issues. Science influences policy and social response; policy and social demand influences the focus and funding on scientific research. The issue of scientific knowledge and uncertainty was mentioned, specifically in relation to the precautionary principle or approach. It is important to remember that science, politics, legal and social factors are all dynamic issues and likely to change in the future. Policies need to be flexible and capable of revision.

Decision makers

There seemed to be a varying opinion as to who or what the main/relevant decision maker was: politicians, authorities, regulators, everybody…

Question 2: How will socio-political factors influence policy development and acceptance?

In answering question two, it was pointed out that socio-political factors have already influenced policy, and that a better question might be how one should ensure that socio-political issues influence policy making in the most constructive and publicly acceptable way. In this respect, a discussion of communication and transparency (already pointed out as important influences under question one) attracted the most attention, and the general consensus was that these were the most important issues. Summaries of a few points are discussed below:

Communicating with the public

Everybody has to answer to the public: scientists, regulators, authorities, politicians, industry, etc. It is important to acknowledge the knowledge and perceptions of the public, not to underestimate their competence, and be aware of the advantages of talking with the public as a source of relevant information for policy building.

Realm of communication

The public is not the only party requiring attention for communication: other parties or stakeholders include the media, regulators, scientists, politicians, operators, NGOs. There is a need for dialogue (communication being a two-way process) between all these parties. There is also a need to distinguish between local, international and global issues: perspectives can change dramatically between different countries, because of economic and political pressure for example.

Specific knowledge and resources

Networks and stakeholder groups are already available in many countries. Although there is pretty good information on the science and environmental risks of radiation exposure, there is very little knowledge on the economic costs and resources that would be necessary were policy changes to be introduced. The next stage should attempt to document some costs in order to facilitate better cost-benefit analysis.

SESSION 4

Strategy to Develop an Efficient System for the Protection of the Environment Against Radiation

Chair: Commissioner Greta Joy Dicus,
Nuclear Regulatory Commission (NRC), USA

HOW COULD THE SYSTEMS FOR THE RADIOLOGICAL PROTECTION OF THE ENVIRONMENT AND OF MAN BE INTEGRATED?

Lars E. Holm

Director General, Swedish Radiation Protection Authority, Sweden
Chairman of the ICRP Task Group on Protection of the Environment

The present situation

There are several reasons why a system for radiological protection of the environment is needed. The current view of the International Commission on Radiological Protection (ICRP) is that "the standards of environmental control needed to protect man to the degree currently thought desirable will ensure that other species are not put at risk".[1] There are clearly situations where this view is insufficient to protect the environment, or even incorrect. This pertains to circumstances where the distribution of the radionuclides in the environment is such that the exposure to man would be minimal, but other organisms in the environment could be considerably exposed. The need to protect the environment in order to safeguard the future well being of man is one of the cornerstones of the Rio Declaration.[2] Also, dose rates received by man are different from those received by other organisms, and the effects endpoints relevant to environmental protection may be completely different from those that are relevant to the protection of man. There are no agreed protection criteria, standards or guidelines with international authority, and it is therefore difficult to provide convincing arguments that the environment will be adequately protected in different circumstances.

Radiological protection of the environment has over the last decade attracted increasing attention. There is rapid progress of the development of approaches to protect the environment, driven to a large extent by the needs of national regulators and of international organisations as part of their initiatives for a sustainable development. The IAEA has addressed environmental protection in several documents, and has just published a report on ethical considerations in protecting the environment from the effects of ionising radiation[3]. The OECD-NEA has pointed out the need to clarify ICRP's current view on environmental protection.[4] The International Union of Radioecology (IUR) has recently organised a consensus conference on the same topic,[5] and an international conferences on the

1. ICRP 1991. 1990 Recommendations of the International Commission on Radiological Protection. Publication 60. Annals of the ICRP 21: 1-3.

2. Rio 1992. United Nations Conference on Environment and Development 1992. The Rio Declaration and the Convention on Biological Diversity. Rio de Janeiro.

3. IAEA 2002. International Atomic Energy Agency. Ethical considerations in protecting the environment from the effects of ionizing radiation. A report for discussion. IAEA-TECDOC-1270.

4. OECD-NEA 2000. A Critical Review of the System of Radiological Protection. OECD-NEA, France.

5. IUR 2001. Radiation Protection in the 21st Century: Ethical, Philosophical and Environmental Issues. Statement from the Consensus Conference. Oslo.

subject will be arranged this year in Australia. The NEA also plans to organise three international fora over the next years in collaboration with the ICRP to discuss radiological protection of the environment. At a national level, authorities are introducing legislation to protect the environment from harmful radiation effects. There is thus already today a risk that this may lead to different scientific and social approaches and make harmonisation with other systems used for environmental protection difficult.

So far, the ICRP has not published any recommendations as to how protection of the environment should be carried out. The Commission has recently set up a Task Group with the aim of developing a protection policy for, and suggesting a framework of, environmental protection in order to feed into the Commission's recommendations for the beginning of the 21st century.[6] This paper provides a progress report of the work of the Task Group.

Protection of the environment

Environmental protection is influenced by a spectrum of cultural and ethical principles and views. The increasing public concern over environmental hazards has led to a variety of national statutory requirements for environmental protection. There is today a generally held view that explicit radiological protection of plants, animals and ecosystems is also needed. The environment is composed of biotic and abiotic components that together form a system, and man is part of and will interact with, this system. The ICRP Task Group is focusing on living organisms, and the impact of ionising radiation upon them. Issues related to protection of the abiotic environment centre largely around the acceptability or not of the presence of radionuclides in the environment, and will be addressed in that context.

The human habitat has been afforded a fairly high level of protection through the application of ICRP's system of protection. However, this habitat is only a part of the total environment, and recent developments require a direct approach in radiological protection to assess and manage environmental effects, to which no guidance can be found in existing recommendations from the ICRP.

Different approaches are being employed to address questions raised with respect to the Commission's current position. They include arguments that because man is protected, therefore all other environmental components are protected. Calculations have demonstrated that, in hypothetical situations and if radionuclide concentrations in the environment are such that man would not receive more than $1mSv\ a^{-1}$, non-human organisms would receive dose-rates that are lower than those likely to cause harm at the population level.[7] In the USA, environmental concentrations has been derived in a tiered approach, based on environmental dose rates considered safe from IAEA studies,[8] and in Canada, target dose rates have been developed for biota based on an ecotoxicological approach

6. ICRP 2001. A report on progress towards new recommendations: a communication from the International Commission on Radiological Protection. J. Radiol. Prot. 21 113-123.

7. IAEA 1992. Effects of Ionising Radiation on Plants and Animals at Levels Implied by Current Radiation Protection Standards. Technical Report 332. IAEA, Vienna.

8. US DoE 2000. DoE Standard. A graded approach for evaluating doses to aquatic and terrestrial biota. US Department of Energy, Washington D.C. (Proposed Standard).

including application of safety factors[9]. Other approaches include the development of a hierarchical system for protection to provide "derived consideration levels" that could be used to help decision making in different circumstances,[10,11] and attempts to produce systematic frameworks for assessing environmental impact of radiation in specific geographic areas.[12]

At the international and national levels, a growing list of animals, plants, areas, and habitats are afforded legal protection from harm from all kinds of activities, including radiation. Therefore, the question whether or not we want to protect individuals, populations, or ecosystems is becoming less important, because of the already existing requirements. Environmental protection has resulted from a mixture of international and national agreements that relate to pollution control, waste management practices, hazard minimisation, and the need to conserve and protect the natural environment with its individual components. These international agreements and conventions already constrain a large number of industrial practices world-wide, and they are usually implemented via more specific national legislation.

At the national level there is also often the requirement to address environmental protection transparently through environmental impact assessments, in order to demonstrate compliance with existing legislation relevant to a practice. With regard to protecting living organisms in terms of "nature conservation", the requirements are usually to *conserve* particular species or habitats; to *maintain the diversity* of habitats, of species, and of the genetic variability within species; and to *protect* habitats and designated areas that are from time to time identified for one reason or another.

The objectives for protecting the environment are usually based on legal requirements that may refer to specific animals and plants at an individual or a population level, or to all animal and plant life within a specific area. There are many radiation effects on fauna and flora that would have to be minimised in order to meet such requirements. Pentreath[13] has suggested that such effects could be summarised into three broad categories: early mortality, reduced reproductive success, and observable cytogenetic effects in order to simplify and enable the development of a management framework. A general category of "morbidity" could be added if the effect did not lead to any of the other categories. These categories comprise many different effects and recognise the limitations of our current knowledge of such effects.

9. Thompson P. and Chamney L. 1999. Environmental protection program to be implemented to fulfil the mandate of the new Canadian Nuclear Safety Commission. In: Proc. Second International Symposium on Ionizing Radiation: Environmental Protection Approaches for Nuclear Facilities, Ottawa, p. 131.

10. Pentreath R.J. 1999. A system for radiological protection of the environment: some initial thoughts and ideas. J. Radiol. Prot. 19:117-128.

11. Pentreath R J 2002. Radiation protection of man and the environment: developing a common approach. J. Radiol. Prot. In press.

12. Strand *et al.,* 2000. Strand P., Brown J.E., Woodhead D.S. and Larsson C.-M. Delivering a system and framework for the protection of the environment from ionising radiation 10th Int. Congress IRPA 14-19 May 2000, Hiroshima, Japan, 2000; P-2a-116, 5.

13. Pentreath R.J. 1999. A system for radiological protection of the environment: some initial thoughts and ideas. J. Radiol. Prot. 19:117-128.

A system of protection is necessary to enable frequent reviews of what we know and do not know about doses and effects on different organisms. It should be applicable to all situations and allow a systematic approach to the derivation and revision of the different parameters that it contains.[14,15]

Some basic elements are:

- a clear set of objectives and principles;

- an agreed set of quantities and units;

- a reference set of dose models for a number of reference fauna and flora;

- a reference set of values to estimate radiation exposure;

- a basic knowledge of radiation effects;

- a means of demonstrating compliance; and

- regular reviews and revisions as new knowledge develops.

A common approach for man and the environment

It will not be possible to provide a general assessment of the radiation effects on the environment as a whole. Instead, Pentreath[16,17] has proposed using a reference set of *dosimetric models* and a reference set of *environmental geometries*, applied to one or more *reference sets of fauna and flora*. This would allow judgements to be made about the probability and severity of radiation effects, as well as an assessment of the likely consequences for either individuals, the population, or for the local environment.

It is knowledge of the dose to, and effects on, representative individuals that forms the initial basis for drawing conclusions on what actions need to be taken in different exposure situations. For human beings, Reference Man[18] is the primary reference for dose assessments, supported by a secondary set of data for a foetus, a child etc. Such data enable dose estimates to be made for "hypothetical" or representative individuals under different circumstances of exposure. For environmental protection, a set of primary Reference Fauna and Flora has proposed that could serve as typical "hypothetical" representatives of animals and plants[19]. A possible set of reference dose models

14. Pentreath R.J. 1999. A system for radiological protection of the environment: some initial thoughts and ideas. J. Radiol. Prot. 19:117-128.

15. Pentreath R.J. 2002. Radiation protection of man and the environment: developing a common approach. J. Radiol. Prot. In press.

16. Pentreath R.J. 1999. A system for radiological protection of the environment: some initial thoughts and ideas. J. Radiol. Prot. 19:117-128.

17. Pentreath R.J. 2002. Radiation protection of man and the environment: developing a common approach. J. Radiol. Prot. In press.

18. ICRP 1975. Report of the Task Group on Reference Man. A report prepared by a task group of Committee 2 *ICRP Publication* 23.

19. Pentreath R.J. 1999. A system for radiological protection of the environment: some initial thoughts and ideas. J. Radiol. Prot. 19:117-128.

and environmental geometries for them has also been suggested,[20] along with the concept that secondary and less complete data sets could also be compiled to reflect different fauna and flora of relevance for specific environmental situations.

The selection criteria for these *primary* reference fauna and flora will include many scientific considerations, and will depend on to what extent they are considered to be *typical* representative fauna or flora of particular ecosystems.[21] The concept of a reference organism is similar to that of ICRP's Reference Man, in that it is intended to act as a basis for calculations and decisions. A reference organism does not represent an average or a sentinel organism, but would serve as a point of reference for making comparisons with other sets of information on other organisms. A reference fauna and flora contains various components. The reference organisms should be "typical" of different habitats and have public or political recognition. It contains reference dose models for different terrestrial and aquatic animals and plants, and reference dose per unit intake (look-up tables), 3-4 "effect" end points, "derived consideration levels", primary and secondary reference fauna and flora.[22] This system makes best use of existing data on doses and effects in other organisms and also identifies gaps for research.

The ICRP Task Group intends to propose a stylised system for radiological protection of the environment, harmonised with the principles for the radiological protection of man along the lines described above. This system will be designed so that it can be integrated with methods that are already in use in some countries. The objectives of a combined approach to the radiological protection of man and the environment might be to

- to safeguard human health by;

- preventing the occurrence of deterministic effects;

- limiting stochastic effects in individuals and minimising them in populations; and

- to safeguard the environment by;

- preventing or reducing the frequency of effects likely to cause early mortality, reduced reproductive success, or the observable cytogenetic effects in individual fauna and flora to a level where they would have a negligible impact on;

- conservation of species, maintenance of biodiversity, or the health and status of natural habitats or communities.

A common approach to the achievement of these objectives could be centred on a set of reference dose models, reference dose per unit intake and external exposure values, plus reference data sets of doses and effects for both man and the environment. The variety of dose models needed for such reference organisms will depend upon the biological effects, and a hierarchy of dose model

---

20. Pentreath R.J. and Woodhead D.S. 2001. A system for protecting the environment from ionising radiation: selecting reference fauna and flora, and the possible dose models and environmental geometries that could be applied to them. Sci. Total Environ. 277:33-43.

21. Strand *et al.,* 2000. Strand P., Brown J.E., Woodhead D.S. and Larsson C.-M. Delivering a system and framework for the protection of the environment from ionising radiation 10th Int. Congress IRPA 14-19 May 2000, Hiroshima, Japan, 2000; P-2a-116, 5.

22. Pentreath R.J. 2002. Radiation protection of man and the environment: developing a common approach. J. Radiol. Prot. In press.

complexity has been suggested by Pentreath & Woodhead.[23] Such models have already been used and form the basis of the current studies being made within EC-funded project FASSET.[24]

Dose consideration levels

For the protection of the public, the ICRP is now discussing an approach based on *Bands of Concern and Protective Action Levels* with reference to background dose rates.[25] This idea is similar to the *Derived Consideration Levels* that have been proposed for fauna and flora to guide the *consideration* of different management options.[26,27] There are today only two factors upon which to assess the potential consequences for fauna and flora: natural background dose rates, and dose rates known to have specific biological effects on individuals. Bands of Derived Consideration Levels for reference fauna and flora could be compiled by combining information on logarithmic bands of dose rates relative to normal natural background dose rates plus information on dose rates that are known to have an adverse biological effect.

Other factors would also have to be taken into account, particularly with regard to the scale of the area affected in terms of elevated dose rates, and the specific nature of the fauna and flora that lived within it. This would also define the boundary between radiation protection expertise and the need for advice that would be provided by others, depending upon the circumstances of the situation. An example of what the Derived Consideration Levels might be for a reference terrestrial mammal sin shown in Table 1 (based on ref. 11). Additions of dose rate that are fractions of normal background would be of little or no concern, whereas dose rates higher than background would be of increasing concern. One advantage of this approach is that for any given spatial and temporal distribution of radionuclides, one should be able to estimate both the relevant bands of concern with respect to both members of the public (based on Reference Man or "secondary" data sets) and the environment (based on primary or secondary Reference Fauna and Flora). These two concepts would be independent of each other, although derived in a complementary manner, and they would each be related to the same concentration of a specific radionuclide, within a specific environmental material, at any particular site (Figure 1).

Discussion

It is evident that a systematic approach is needed in order to provide high-level advice and guidance. This should ideally include the following: a clear set of principles and objectives; an agreed terminology (particularly with regard to quantities and units); reference dose models and related data

23. Strand *et al.,* 2000. Strand P., Brown J.E., Woodhead D.S. and Larsson C.-M. Delivering a system and framework for the protection of the environment from ionising radiation 10th Int. Congress IRPA 14-19 May 2000, Hiroshima, Japan, 2000; P-2a-116, 5.

24. Copplestone *et al.,* 2001. Copplestone D., Beilby S., Jones S.R., Patton D., Daniel P., and Gize I., 2001. Impact Assessment of Ionising Radiation on Wildlife. R&D Publication 128, Environment Agency, Bristol, United Kingdom.

25. ICRP 2001. A report on progress towards new recommendations: a communication from the International Commission on Radiological Protection. J. Radiol. Prot. 21 113-123.

26. Pentreath R.J. 1999. A system for radiological protection of the environment: some initial thoughts and ideas. J. Radiol. Prot. 19:117-128.

27. Pentreath R.J. 2002. Radiation protection of man and the environment: developing a common approach. J. Radiol. Prot. In press.

sets to estimate exposures; biological end points (radiation effects); data relevant to the needs of environmental protection; guidance on the practical application of the system; plus clear ownership and management of review and revision processes in the light of new data and interpretations.

Given the speed with which radiological protection of the environment is developing, and the lack of any systematic and structured approaches that have wide support, there are strong expectations from many quarters on the ICRP to act. No doubt, the Commission is best placed for providing guidance that could be globally accepted and that could also synthesise human and environmental radiological protection into a coherent framework. A prerequisite is that ICRP acknowledges both the need for guidance by regulators and implementers, and for public awareness and concern in this matter. This would require that the ICRP system for assessments be expanded to incorporate the environment, that a system for evaluation of environmental risks is developed, and that a new system for managing environmental risks be formed. In the latter case, the ICRP must considerably recognise its appreciation of developments in other fields.

If the ICRP were to widen its scope of activities and address directly radiological protection of all living organisms, international and national authorities would welcome such a commitment. The Commission has a long experience on which such a system of protection could be built. This would add credibility both to the environmental protection among those working with radiation, and to the Commission among those working with other sectors of environmental protection. For the regulators and the industry, an ICRP initiative would increase the possibilities of demonstrating compliance with environmental requirements relating to release of radionuclides into the environment. It would also provide advice in intervention situations on how to deal with questions relating to certain segments of the environment. Finally, it could also be used to inform stakeholders and help bring the radiological protection more in line with the regulation of other potentially damaging industrial practices or of other contaminants associated with practices of interest to the Commission.

For the ICRP, another consequence would be the need to demonstrate its commitment for environmental protection. This commitment must be reflected in the organisation of the Commission's work and in the composition of experts. It would require expertise in radioecology, radiobiology, ecotoxicology, dosimetry to deal with issues relating to the environment, such as estimating exposures, identifying data on biological effects and developing dose models for reference organisms.

The Commission's system of protection has evolved over time as new evidence has become available and as our understanding of underlying mechanisms has increased. Consequently the Commission's risk estimates have been revised regularly, and substantial revisions are made at intervals of about 10-15 years. It is therefore likely that any system designed for the radiological protection of the environment would also take time to develop, and similarly be subject to revision as new information is obtained and experience gained in putting it into practice.

References

ICRP 1991. 1990 Recommendations of the International Commission on Radiological Protection. Publication 60. Annals of the ICRP 21:1-3.

Rio 1992. United Nations Conference on Environment and Development 1992. The Rio Declaration and the Convention on Biological Diversity. Rio de Janeiro.

IAEA 2002. International Atomic Energy Agency. Ethical considerations in protecting the environment from the effects of ionising radiation. A report for discussion. IAEA-TECDOC-1270.

OECD-NEA 2000. A Critical Review of the System of Radiological Protection. OECD-NEA, France.

IUR 2001. Radiation Protection in the 21st Century: Ethical, Philosophical and Environmental Issues. Statement from the Consensus Conference. Oslo.

ICRP 2001. A report on progress towards new recommendations: a communication from the International Commission on Radiological Protection J. Radiol. Prot. 21:113-123.

IAEA 1992. Effects of Ionising Radiation on Plants and Animals at Levels Implied by Current Radiation Protection Standards. Technical Report 332. IAEA, Vienna.

US DoE 2000. DoE Standard. A graded approach for evaluating doses to aquatic and terrestrial biota. US Department of Energy, Washington D.C. (Proposed Standard).

Thompson P. and Chamney L. 1999. Environmental protection program to be implemented to fulfil the mandate of the new Canadian Nuclear Safety Commission. In: Proc. Second International Symposium on Ionizing Radiation: Environmental Protection Approaches for Nuclear Facilities, Ottawa, p. 131.

Pentreath R.J. 1999. A system for radiological protection of the environment: some initial thoughts and ideas. J. Radiol. Prot. 19:117-128.

Pentreath R.J. 2002. Radiation protection of man and the environment: developing a common approach. J. Radiol. Prot. In press.

Strand et al., 2000. Strand P, Brown J E, Woodhead D S and Larsson C-M Delivering a system and framework for the protection of the environment from ionising radiation 10th Int. Congress IRPA 14-19 May 2000, Hiroshima, Japan, 2000; P-2a-116, 5.

ICRP 1975. Report of the Task Group on Reference Man. A report prepared by a task group of Committee 2 ICRP Publication 23.

Pentreath R J and Woodhead D S 2001. A system for protecting the environment from ionising radiation: selecting reference fauna and flora, and the possible dose models and environmental geometries that could be applied to them. Sci. Total Environ. 277:33-43.

Copplestone et al., 2001. Copplestone D, Beilby S, Jones SR, Patton D, Daniel P, and Gize I 2001. Impact Assessment of Ionising Radiation on Wildlife. R&D Publication 128, Environment Agency, Bristol, United Kingdom.

Table 1. An example of derived consideration levels for a reference terrestrial mammal (based on reference 11)

Consideration level	Dose rate increment of annual dose	Likely effect on individuals	Aspects of concern
Level 5	>1000	Early mortality	Possible remedial action considered
Level 4	>100	Reduced reproductive success	Concern dependent on what fauna and flora, and their numbers, likely to be affected
Level 3	>10	Observable cytogenetic effects	Action dependent upon size and nature of area affected
Level 2 (baseline)	Normal background		Some action considered
Level 1	<background	Low-trivial	No action considered

Figure 1. **Developing a combined approach for the radiological protection of man and the environment (based on reference 11)**

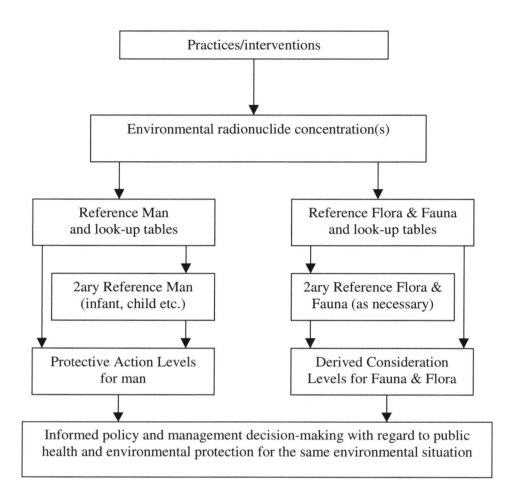

STAKEHOLDER INVOLVEMENT IN DEVELOPING ENVIRONMENTAL RADIATION PROTECTION POLICY AND RECOMMENDATIONS

John Till
Risk Assessment Corporation, USA

It is appropriate that as the last technical speaker on the programme, I have the privilege of speaking to you about the role of stakeholders in developing recommendations for protection of the environment. It is appropriate because regardless of the resources, the time, and the excellent science we invest in developing recommendations, if we do so without involving the broad variety of individuals who will ultimately be implementing and judging them, we will fall short of our goal. Therefore, this presentation encourages you to think about why stakeholder involvement is critical to our success.

Before launching into this discussion on "stakeholder" involvement, it is important to define this term that is not easily translated into many other languages. One direct translation of a "stake" is a pointed piece of wood or post. In the early days of America, settlers would mark their property with stakes, often referred to as "staking their claims". The property was also called their "stake." As defined by *Webster's Dictionary*, a stakeholder is a "person entrusted with the stakes of two or more betters".

The word stakeholder has been popularised in recent years to refer to individuals who have something invested in an issue at hand. I'd like to define, clearly, what I mean by "stakeholder" for the purpose of this paper.

Definition: Stakeholders are individuals who have a personal, financial, health, or legal interest in policy or recommendations that affect their well-being or that of their environment. Used broadly, this includes any party who has an interest in the issue at hand.

Perhaps in our deliberations in the future we will create a better word than stakeholder to describe more universally what we mean. For now, I offer and use this definition.

Next, it is important to make clear what we are talking about when we say stakeholder involvement, with the emphasis on *involvement*.

In 1988, I was abruptly introduced to stakeholders who believed they had been severely and unknowingly exposed to radionuclides released at an U.S. Government facility (Till 1995). I was the Chairman of the Technical Steering Panel for the Hanford Environmental Dose Reconstruction Project. The Technical Steering Panel had been created to independently direct a study to reconstruct doses to the public who lived around the Hanford Nuclear Site. Hanford is part of the U.S. Department of Energy's nuclear weapons complex, and it released large amounts of radioiodine and other materials during its early years of operation. I did not know how to work with stakeholders at that time. My initial approach to stakeholder involvement was to use a formal setting with the public speaking from a podium and the Technical Steering Panel seated behind tables. We were frequently challenged because of the historical events that had occurred, even though we were an independent panel of scientists charged with finding the truth about the releases of radionuclides and resulting doses. This was *not* stakeholder involvement!

I learned quickly that the only way to build credibility was to get the public involved in the process of the science being undertaken. Very early in our study we sought to involve the public in every possible aspect of the work. We held frequent meetings to listen to public concerns and discuss the ongoing work. All meetings were open. These steps significantly altered the environment in which we were working and created a strong sense of ownership of the work for many members of the public who did not trust us at the beginning of the project.

This lesson about public involvement at Hanford was expanded further in a dose reconstruction project that focused on the Savannah River Site, another facility in the U.S. nuclear weapons complex. Our goal was to begin the project with as much stakeholder involvement as possible. The first task for this project was to review and catalogue all of the historical records on site, amounting to almost 50,000 boxes of historical records (Till 1997). Each box had to be reviewed for content and entered into a database for future retrieval in our study. With the cooperation of management at the site, we invited stakeholders representing several groups of citizens to watch as we reviewed historical records during the early stages of the project. This step clearly showed the stakeholders what was involved in reviewing historical records and how tedious the process really was. Although the stakeholders' interest in watching us review historical records soon dwindled, providing them an opportunity to watch first hand helped achieve credibility and led to a positive and fruitful interaction with the public during the course of the project. This is what I mean by stakeholder involvement; in short, actively engaging interested parties during the evolution of the work.

In laying the framework for this presentation, it is also important to understand when stakeholders should be a part of the policy and recommendation process. In my view, stakeholders should be involved if they or their environment are the target of the risk. Therefore, not every situation is amenable to involving stakeholders. Since our research team has focused its work on estimating risks to members of the public, stakeholder involvement has been a key element of almost all of our work.

To understand the role of stakeholders in developing radiation protection policy and recommendations, it is helpful to ask ourselves three questions:

- Do you believe stakeholders can play a role in making policy recommendations and help us make better decisions about protecting the environment?

- Do you believe stakeholders can help us conduct better scientific studies and produce results that can be used in making recommendations about protection of the environment?

- Do you believe by involving stakeholders in the decisions and recommendations we make today, they will be more enduring and better accepted in the future?

This discussion addresses these questions through examples of stakeholder involvement.

Do you believe stakeholders can play a role in making policy recommendations and help us make better decisions about protecting the environment?

This question may be addressed by an example from a project in which our research team was hired to work with stakeholders to independently recommend cleanup levels for the Rocky Flats Environmental Technology Site near Denver, Colorado in the U.S. (Till and Meyer 2001). This former nuclear weapons complex facility historically housed plutonium fabrication operations, resulting in contamination of the site. The facility is currently being closed down and cleaned up. It is located just 26 km from Denver, and the land currently occupied by the site will be of extreme economic importance for the region in the future.

The Rocky Flats Soil Action Level Oversight Panel directed our study (Figure 1). The Panel of stakeholders represented a cross section of the community, consisting of a mix of technical specialists and people with no technical experience drawn from public interest groups, local governments, and the general pubic. The three responsible agencies (the U.S. Department of Energy, the U.S. Environmental Protection Agency, and the Colorado Department of Public Health and Environment) were each represented by one ex-officio member, making the total Panel membership 16 people. The Panel met for work sessions with my research team on a monthly basis between October 1998 and March 2000, with all meetings open to the public. During this time, the stakeholders became familiar with technical terms, such as uncertainty, concentration factors, breathing rates, and re-suspension, which were crucial to determining a level for cleanup.

In this example, it is important to recognize that although not all of the stakeholders had detailed knowledge of the science that was being conducted, they firmly grasped the significance of the most important components and how changes in these components affected the final result.

Figure 1. **The rocky flats soil action level oversight panel**

For example, Figure 2 shows how we presented uncertainty, as a probability of exceeding the dose limit as a function of the cleanup level. Distributions were developed for different scenarios of exposure. The stakeholders decided that they wanted a 10% probability level, that is, a 90% probability of not exceeding the dose limit. In setting this level, the stakeholders recognized that the dose limit could be exceeded 10% of the time. Therefore, they acknowledged that dose limits may be exceeded because of the uncertainties of the real world. The concept of uncertainty is often difficult to explain, but the stakeholders readily accepted this approach.

What evolved was a strong endorsement by the Panel for a cleanup level of about 1 300 Bq g^{-1}. We made it clear that there could not be a single value for soil cleanup, but that any value within a general range of between 1 000 and 2 300 Bq g^{-1} would likely be acceptable.

Figure 2. **Graphic illustrating the bounding scenarios and showing a range of possible soil action levels centred around about 1300 Bq kg^{-1}, which is the 10% probability level for the rancher scenario and child scenarios.**

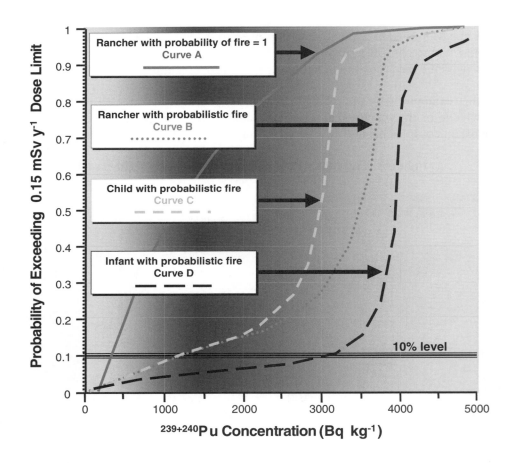

Rocky Flats is a perfect example illustrating that stakeholders can play a role in making policy recommendations about protection of the environment and that we can make better decisions with stakeholder involvement. This experience at Rocky Flats could be used as a model for stakeholder involvement. It shows that the process of stakeholder involvement, if conducted with a deliberate set of ground rules to follow, can be effective in making recommendations and decisions about risk.

Do you believe stakeholders can help us conduct better scientific studies and produce results that can be used in making recommendations about protection of the environment?

To address this question, I return to the example of the Hanford Site in the State of Washington. During the historical dose reconstruction at Hanford, we realised early on that very little knowledge was available about the habits and diets of Native Americans who lived along and extensively used the Columbia River near the Hanford Site. The facility had released significant quantities of radionuclides to the Columbia River and to the atmosphere during the early years of operations.

This area of the U.S. is one of the great cultural regions for our Native American people. In fact, much of the land around the Hanford Site is owned or ceded to the U.S. Government by Native American Tribes of the region.

There was concern by Native Americans that because their unique lifestyles relied more heavily on natural sources of local foods and materials and they had unique pathways of exposure, their risk may have been significantly greater than that of non-native American people. Working with nine Tribes in the region, we collected and summarized data, which allowed us to include information on diet, lifestyle, and special cultural ceremonies in our research.

There were several pathways, in particular, for which we had little data and for which Native Americans wanted information about risk. We were asked to study exposure from shoreline sediment used for paints and medicinal purposes, sweat lodges using Columbia River water, and inhalation of river water spray during fishing. The pathway of most concern was that of fish consumption, not only because of the large quantities of fish consumed, but also because they consumed the whole fish. Table 1 shows fish consumption data we gathered with the involvement of Native Americans and used in our risk estimates.

Table 1. **Fish consumption of Native Americans for the Columbia River near the Hanford Site as reported by Walker and Pritchard (1999)**

Fish Category[a]	Jan	Feb	Mar	Apr	May	Jun	Jul	Aug	Sep	Oct	Nov	Dec	Total	Holdup[b] (days)
Omnivore	4	4	4	2	2	2	2	2	2	2	4	4	34	3
1st order predator	--	--	--	--	--	--	--	--	--	--	--	--	0	0
2nd order predator	4	4	4	2	2	2	2	2	2	2	4	4	34	3
Salmon	3	3	3	22	22	22	22	22	22	22	3	3	169	14

[a] Omnivorous fish include bullhead, catfish, suckers, whitefish, chiselmouth, chub, sturgeon, minnows and shiners, First-order predators include perch, crappie, punkinseed and bluegill. Second-order predators include bass, trout and squawfish.
[b] The time between obtaining fish from the river and consuming it

Our calculations indicated that the risks from all pathways would be small, except for the consumption of fish from the river. In the case of risk from consumption of fish, risks to Native Americans could have been substantially greater than those of non-native American people. Since the purpose of this study was to be a screening analysis, it was evident that the only pathway that deserved more detailed analysis, if quantitative estimates of risks were warranted, was consumption of fish from the Columbia River.

This example emphasises that stakeholders can provide critical information in risk analysis and can help us conduct more defensible science. Although this is just one example of the stakeholders' role on science and decision making, it has been our experience that in every case where stakeholders are engaged in the scientific process, a better product has evolved.

Do you believe by involving stakeholders in the decisions and recommendations we make today, they will be more enduring and better accepted in the future?

Of course there is no way to conclusively answer this question, and only time will tell. However, I do have an example that provides some insight.

In 1995, a lawsuit was filed by a local citizens' group alleging that the Los Alamos National Laboratory was not in compliance with the requirements prescribed by the Clean Air Act for Radionuclides. The suit was settled through an agreement that called for a series of independent audits. Our research team was asked by both parties to be the auditor. The question that we were charged with answering was, "Did Los Alamos National Laboratory meet requirements for compliance with 40 CFR 61, Subpart H (US EPA 1989), for the year 1996?" The settlement agreement also provided that we were to be observed during the audit by representatives of the citizens' group to verify the integrity of the audit.

Los Alamos must maintain a high degree of security because of its mission and the nature of research that is undertaken, and, therefore, it is neither open to the public nor has it traditionally encouraged public participation in many site-related activities. The audit process included site visits and tours of facilities, document review and retrieval, and interviews with staff.

It is easy to imagine the complex situation that existed. Not only did we have to carry out the audit, but the citizens' group that had filed the lawsuit required that we perform the audit under their observation and that we communicate our activities associated with the audit.

We quickly became overwhelmed with questions raised by the stakeholders' representatives. Therefore, we agreed that as part of the audit we would answer questions provided in writing. Ultimately, the stakeholders submitted 75 questions that we responded to in our report. The documentation of stakeholder questions was critical to our success and added significantly to their understanding of the audit process and to the credibility of the audit itself.

Regular work sessions were held where we allowed the stakeholders to join us and look at how we were evaluating compliance. Although we found the process tedious at first, once we laid out a plan for the audit, announced our schedule of visits, and clearly established the rules to be followed, it was an orderly and rather quick process. We have now conducted two audits and are conducting the third audit this year.

What does the Los Alamos audit tell us about how involving stakeholders today can help us make better and more enduring decisions for the future? What is so remarkable about this example is that when we began our first audit of Los Alamos National Laboratory, the attitude toward any involvement of the public in compliance issues was defensive and closed. Scientists from the Laboratory did not see how the public could play a role in their compliance with the regulation. They saw it as strictly a regulatory and technical matter.

This year we will complete our third independent audit at Los Alamos. I am pleased to report that the stakeholders and scientists have worked together to develop a new relationship. Local stakeholder groups and Los Alamos scientists are meeting regularly to discuss issues openly and to improve communication about the audit process. Although the legal settlement agreement in 1997 states that a total of four audits may be conducted, our plan is to establish a model where local stakeholders and the Laboratory can carry on without us. We are hopeful this can be accomplished. We also believe that if this new relationship is successful, the Los Alamos example will change the way compliance is evaluated. Demonstrating compliance will become a more participatory process and will produce a more defensible and enduring result. Our experience at Los Alamos illustrates how stakeholders can help us make better and more enduring decisions.

These three examples show stakeholder involvement clearly has made a difference in science and decision-making. What have not been discussed are the pain, the frustration, and the extensive time required to involve stakeholders in science. Also, as scientists, we are often not well equipped to take on this new and demanding aspect to our work.

Let me caution you that stakeholder involvement is neither public relations nor is it an excuse for investing fewer resources into science because you can get by with a lower quality product. Indeed, the expectations for the product, whether they include recommendations for protection of the environment or demonstration of compliance, are even tougher to meet.

How do we involve stakeholders in developing environmental radiation protection policy and recommendations? First, we must believe the answer to each of the three questions discussed is, "Yes".

Second, we must have some guidelines within which to work. Although these are evolving as we learn more with each study, six key guidelines for working with stakeholders are to

- Recognise the difficulty of this commitment.

- Understand that short term costs are greater.

- Clearly define the role and authority of stakeholders.

- Develop a plan for receiving and responding to stakeholder input.

- Have a well-defined schedule and end product.

- Recognise that once stakeholder involvement is made you cannot retract the commitment.

In conclusion, it appears from the attendance at this meeting that both NEA and ICRP are taking a very proactive approach to stakeholder involvement. I am confident this is an intelligent decision and that a better product will be the result. Hopefully, this presentation will help provide some insight and guidance on this important facet of all scientists' work.

References

Till, J.E. 1995. "Building Credibility in Public Studies." *American Scientist* 83 (5). Magazine of Sigma Xi. The Scientific Research Society.

Till, J.E. 1997. "Environmental Dose Reconstruction." *Proceedings of the Thirty-First Annual Meeting of the National Council on Radiation Protection and Measurements (NCRP).* Washington, DC, April 12–13, 1995. National Council on Radiation Protection and Measurements, Bethesda, Maryland.

Till, J.E. and K.R. Meyer. 2001. "Public Involvement in Science and Decision Making." *Health Physics.* Vol. 80 (4): 370–379.

US EPA (U.S. Environmental Protection Agency). 1989. 40 CFR Part 61. *National Emission Standards for Hazardous Air Pollutants; Radionuclides; Final Rule and Notice of Reconsideration.* US EPA, Washington, DC.

Walker, D.E. Jr. and L.W. Pritchard. 1999. *Estimated Radiation Doses to Yakama Tribal Fishermen: A Test Application of the Columbia River Dosimetry Model Developed for the Hanford Environmental Dose Reconstruction Project.* Boulder: Walker Research Group, Ltd.

PANEL DISCUSSION*

What are the characteristics of the process for developing a system of radiological protection of the environment?

It is agreed that the protection system for man works well and is broadly accepted. But it is believed by the majority of participants that this system is not necessarily an adequate approach, especially for environmental systems where man is absent. Nevertheless it should be a good starting point for the development of a protection system of the environment. Basically a system is needed which:

- is broadly understood and harmonised by the international community;

- does not bind significant human and financial resources, e.g. for intensive monitoring.

The representative of FASSET even sees the possibility that an effective system could save manpower and money.

A central point in the consideration is that the aim of environmental protection is widely agreed, but the objectives are not clearly defined. Corresponding suggestions have been rare in the meeting. It is still open what kind of effects should be considered in an assessment statement. Do we have to protect individuals, population species and/or ecosystems and which dose or environmental contamination limits will be appropriate? The recommendations given have been more of a general nature, e.g. it will be necessary to collect and to structure all available information for a better understanding of the system.

It has to be recognised that a certain state of environmental protection has already been established, due to the limitation of dose to man and due to advanced techniques. But their improvement and development are not always respected in the discussions. According to the literature reviews by IAEA and UNSCEAR, an upper maximum dose of 1 mGy/d to terrestrial and aquatic organisms would not lead to visible effects. It has to be pointed out, however, that the corresponding level of radionuclides in the environment would be unacceptably high. Even if dose limits for the environment would be one or two orders of magnitude lower, corresponding release rates would not represent the technical state of the art.

The representatives of ICRP stressed that it is the task of ICRP to give advice and to develop protection systems. Guidance on the protection of the environment is part of the protection systems, and consequently an essential task of the commission.

---

* Kindly provided by Erich Wirth.

The path forward

Concerning the question in the path forward, it has to be realised that countries are in different stages with respect to environmental protection. It is the task of the international organisations to bring them together for consensus by promoting the discussion. The system has to be developed in an open dialogue. The safety standards have to be implemented. It is believed that the development of recommendations will take time, at least about one decade. An involvement of stakeholders into this process is highly appreciated.

For radiological statements about the impact of radionuclides on nature, it is suggested to develop assessment tools which are widely agreed. One panel member figured out that protection of the environment means to keep at least the radionuclide concentration in the environment on low levels. For existing situations, restoration has to be taken into account. For ongoing practices, the annual release rates should be limited on world wide accepted upper levels. After a broad acceptance of a dose limit for man of about 0.3 mSv/a, the derivation of upper release rates for different types of plants, independent of their location, would be the next consequent step forward.

SYNTHESIS OF THE FORUM

SUMMARY COMMENTS

Rick Jones
Chair, CRPPH

In the closing session of the NEA/ICRP Forum, the Chair of the CRPPH summarised that during the conduct of the First NEA Forum on Radiological Protection of the Environment, participant comments could be grouped around the common themes of: **Challenges** facing us; **Characteristics** participants would be looking for in any proposed ICRP recommendations for radiological protection of the environment; and **Opportunities** for organisations to proceed. Each theme will be discussed below in turn.

Challenges

The following challenges in formulating any new ICRP recommendations for the radiological protection of the environment are shared by many of those who participated in this forum:

- Identification and communication of the bases for any new ICRP recommendations.

  - Missing from the current system is a demonstration that the existing ICRP recommendations are adequately protecting the environment, through the protection of humankind.

  - Current anthropocentric ICRP recommendations do not explicitly address radiological impacts: 1) where the human is absent; 2) where humans have been removed from the environment; 3) where human exposure is low; and where environmental exposures are elevated (i.e., in cases where the pathways of exposure to biota are different than the pathway of exposure to humans).

  - Addressing issues (a) and (b) may not require an entire new ICRP recommendation based upon a "standard reference man" dosimetry approach for biota.

- Any new system should enhance and build upon the long history of national programs dealing with radiological protection of the environment.

- Our capability to detect radiation exceeds our ability to determine any harm associated with the presence of low levels of radiation. Great care should be exercised by the ICRP to clarify when the presence of environmental sources of radiation are sufficient to require regulation.

- ICRP may be able to contribute to international harmony in the radiological protection of the environment and humankind in order to support commerce and industry. Actions should acknowledge and support globalisation.

- Clarity is needed to define the endpoints and goals of any new ICRP recommendations. Publication of recommendations for ease in generating a compliance based program to facilitate regulations may not be appropriate to the risks to the environment from radiological releases and operations. ICRP adoption of a performance-based approach to radiological protection of the environment may be more appropriate to the hazard presented.

- A program to validate the statements of the existing ICRP recommendations may be a more prudent strategy for the radiological protection of the environment and in any case is a necessary first step in determining if a "standard reference man" approach should subsequently be developed for biota.

- ICRP should initiate enhanced communications with policy makers and the public to assure any actions taken by ICRP are responsive to their needs.

- ICRP should demonstrate that any recommendations they may publish are a valid use of societies resources (i.e., funds and personnel) with a commensurate improvement in public and environmental health and safety.

- ICRP should take a global overall view in addressing this subject by considering and weighing the views of all interested parties in this debate and not be unduly influenced by any particular special or vocal interest groups.

- ICRP should develop a strategy for engagement of stakeholders in formulation of potential recommendations and should communicate that strategy to stakeholders to apprise them of opportunities for participation in the process.

If these challenges are not dealt with in a productive and constructive manner by the ICRP, the immediate and long-term credibility of the ICRP may be at risk.

Characteristics

Based upon discussions at the Forum, participants will be looking for the following characteristics of any new ICRP recommendations for the radiological protection of the environment:

- Sound scientific bases for any proposed environmental recommendations.

- Holistic approaches that strike a balance and integrates with other environmental impacts for a consistent approach to the protection of the environment. Any new framework should allow for a proportionate approach to the environmental hazards present.

- Flexibility in any proposed system that allows for case-by-case actions and the ability to use field data to enhance and refine programs as implementation lessons learned and data are obtained, investigated and analysed.

- Clear definitive statements as to how and where proposed recommendations, if any, are to be applied and why.

- A clear assessment phase that supports a decision phase with specific criteria as the bases for action.

- Encourages an iterative program that collects lessons learned in establishing a program of continuous improvement.

- Any assumptions and uncertainties associated with creating proposed ICRP recommendations are clearly stated and actions initiated to better inform and clarify these issues. This will identify the line between science and policy and be of particular interest to policy makers at the national level.

- Any proposed environmental recommendations should support sustainable development.

- As was the case at this NEA/ICRP Forum, ICRP should continue an aggressive, transparent, and inclusive process to fully communicate with all stakeholders on the creation and bases for any new recommendations.

- Any new ICRP recommendations should be forward thinking, looking at a longer time scale for the applicability of their recommendations and have built-in flexibility to accommodate future changes in society and science (e.g., genetic research).

- Acknowledge and encourage a phased or tiered approach to evaluating potential impacts to the environment, and to the amount of environmental monitoring that may be needed in support of the potential recommendations, to reduce the impact of the monitoring program on the environment.

- Consider the *Precautionary Principle* and provide clarity on its use and application to radiological protection of the environment.

Any proposed ICRP recommendations should be receptive to the use of the new ICRP methodologies of MUM (Meet, Understand and Modify) rather than the previous protocols of DAD (Declare, Announce and Defend).

Opportunities

Based upon discussions at the Forum, participants identified numerous opportunities to team with and assist the ICRP in being responsive to these issues for any new ICRP recommendations for the radiological protection of the environment:

- Some environmental models exist, or are in development, that will facilitate decision making in the efficient and cost effective implementation of any new ICRP recommendations for the radiological protection of the environment. Examples include FASSET, DOE and UK. The ICRP should facilitate and encourage communication among the sponsors of these approaches, and should maintain an understanding of the advantages and opportunities presented by each approach in shaping their proposed recommendations for environmental protection of the environment.

- To enhance acceptance and understanding when ICRP chooses to publish any new, proposed set of recommendation for the radiological protection of the environment, ICRP should include not only the recommendations themselves but a clear discussion of: (1) the scientific bases forming the foundation for the recommendations; (2) cost analysis to demonstrate the appropriate use of public funds; (3) a discussion of any trade-offs made; and (4) a communications package for the recommendation with clear language for each audience that explains the value added for the publication of proposed environmental recommendations.

- Continue liaison and co-operation with organisations such as those represented at this NEA/ICRP Forum that will be affected by the recommendations, including policy makers, national regulators, implementers (including industry), the press, public and others to create support for acceptance and timely implementation of any new ICRP recommendations for the radiological protection of the environment.

The Committee on Radiation Protection and Public Health (CRPPH), of the Nuclear Energy Agency (NEA) represents 27 member states having the greatest capital investment in nuclear power and is committed to work with the ICRP to address shortfalls in the current set of ICRP recommendations to assure the public of the radiological protection of the environment.

It is critically important to future generations that during this time of global conflict and competition for resources, including energy, that we do not take international actions that preclude national prerogatives concerning the appropriate mix of energy sources needed to promote national interests while not impacting our surrounding environment.

WHAT DO WE KNOW? WHERE DO WE GO FROM HERE? IMPLICATIONS FOR ICRP DEVELOPMENTS

Roger Clarke

Chairman, International Commission on Radiological Protection

Introduction

This first NEA forum is "In collaboration with ICRP" and we wanted views from participants regarding our initiative on radiological protection of the environment. The members of the Main Commission of ICRP who have attended this forum have been delighted with the outcome. ICRP has a range of options for its future activity with regard to radiological protection of the environment, starting with withdrawing altogether from the subject, through maintaining our current assertion, to fully developing a new policy. I am very pleased that, this week, all the contributions have been so positive and supportive of ICRP taking the initiative to develop an international policy.

What have we learned?

There is no single ethic that encapsulates what is meant by protection of the environment. The basis for its protection can be traced back to

- scientific evidence;

- social and cultural concerns, which have their basis in religious or philosophical tenets and beliefs;

- the need to comply with international and national law that has arisen with respect to the protection and conservation of the environment.

We learned of the research that can underpin the establishment of databases such as that for the FASSET project. However, until we have decided what it is we want to protect and what principles are established to enable assessments to be made, we cannot evaluate those data.

Emerging issues for ICRP

The particular issues that we have identified that are relevant to the future ICRP programme begin with the need to ensure that the radiological principles must be consistent with international views on the inter-dependence of mankind and the environment. We must show how knowledge of the potential effects of radiation on the environment can be used to inform decision making and the public by the development of the techniques we have heard for stakeholder involvement.

The principles must be practical and flexible in operation and should apply first to the routine situations that designers of facilities have to meet. They should also provide advice in intervention situations for taking action to protect the environment. There will need to be guidance to help to demonstrate compliance with existing environmental requirements. As a result of these considerations, the radiological basis should be in line with the regulation of other potentially damaging practices. The ideas should not be overly complex and there should be a proportionate response.

A system for protection of the environment

The emerging consensus from this meeting would suggest that the key elements of a system would involve:

- a clear set of objectives and principles;
- an agreed set of quantities and units;
- a reference set of dose models for a defined number of reference fauna and flora;
- basic knowledge of radiation effects;
- a means of demonstrating compliance;
- regular reviews and revisions as new knowledge develops.

This system, which clearly has the unanimous support of the meeting, requires the establishment of reference fauna and flora. These will have to be "typical" of different habitats and will have to be accepted by both the public and politicians. There will be reference dose models, which need reference dose per unit intake or exposure coefficients (look-up tables). We are apparently agreeing on 3-4 "effect" end points and the suggestion has been made for "Derived consideration levels", based on multiples of the natural background radiation exposures to which all fauna and flora are subject.

The parallels with the current ICRP work on dose/unit intake by Reference Man are clear. Indeed it could be foreseen that there would be primary and secondary reference flora and fauna. In carrying out this work, we must make best use of existing data and identify gaps for research.

Objectives for a common approach

Summarising then what I see emerging as an initial philosophy for ICRP is

To safeguard human health by

- preventing the occurrence of deterministic effects; and
- reducing the frequency of stochastic effects.

To safeguard the environment by

- preventing, or reducing to a level where they would have a negligible impact, the frequency of effects likely to cause early mortality, reduced reproductive success, or the occurrence of cytogenetic effects in individual fauna and flora;

- promoting the conservation of species;

- maintaining biodiversity, or the health and status of natural habitats or communities.

ICRP and protection of the environment

Finally in developing its policy, ICRP must show its commitment for protection of the environment and this undertaking must be reflected in the organisation of its work and in the composition of both the Main Commission and its standing Committees.

The Commission is expecting to receive a first draft of the report from its Task Group on protection of the environment later this year (2002). This will be made available on our website for wide consultation. I hope that by the second NEA Forum, comments will be available from CRPPH members and others so that the debate may be pursued in order to agree a policy for radiological protection of the environment.

LIST OF PARTICIPANTS

AUSTRALIA

BURNS, Peter A.
Director Environmental & Radiation
Health Branch
ARPANSA
Lower Plenty Road
Yallambie – Victoria 3085

Tel: +61 3 9433 2335
Fax: +61 3 9432 1835
E-mail: peter.burns@health.gov.au

GARRETT, Wayne
Counsellor (Nuclear)
Australian High Commission
ANSTO Office, Australia House
Strand
London WC2B 4LA

Tel: +44 (20) 7887 57 59
Fax: +44 (20) 7873 90 26
E-mail: wayne.garrett@dfat.gov.au

AUSTRIA

KATZLBERGER, Christian
Bundesamt f. Landwirtschaft
Spargelfeldstrasse 192
A-1226 Vienna

Tel: +43 1 73216 3224
Fax: +43 1 73216 3225
E-mail: christian.katzlberger@relay.bfl.at

BELGIUM

CLAES, Jurgen
Agence Fédérale de Contrôle Nucléaire
36, Rue Ravenstein
B-1000 Bruxelles

Tel: +32 (0) 22 89 21 59
Fax: +32 (0) 22 89 21 52
E-mail: Jurgen.Claes@Fanc.fgov.be

CANADA

GRAHAM, Robert D.
Atomic Energy of Canada Ltd
(AECL)
Chalk River Laboratories
Station 19
KOJ 1PO Chalk River, Ontario

Tel: +1 613 584 3311 Ext 3682
Fax: +1 613 584 4108
E-mail: grahamrd@aecl.ca

CZECH REPUBLIC

HULKA, Jiri
National Radiation Protection Institute
(SURO)
Srobárova 48
100 00 Prague

Tel: +420 602 295 421
Fax: +420 49 56 11 227
E-mail: JHulka@suro.cz

RULIK, Petr
Head of Division
National Radiation Protection Inst.
(SURO)
Srobarova 48
100 00 Prague

Tel: +420 2 6708 2478
Fax: +420 2 6731 1410
E-mail: prulik@suro.cz

DENMARK

LAURIDSEN, Bente
Senior Health Physicist
AHF-214
Risø National Laboratory
DK-4000 Roskilde

Tel: +45 46 77 43 09
Fax: +45 46 77 43 43
E-mail: bente.lauridsen@risoe.dk

FINLAND

HANNINEN, Riitta
Radiation and Nuclear Safety
Authority (STUK)
P.O. Box 14
00881 Helsinki

Tel: +358(9)7598 8312
Fax: +358(9)7598 8498
E-mail: riitta.hanninen@stuk.fi

FRANCE

BARESCUT, Jean-Claude
IPSN / DPRE
Dpt de protection de l'environnement
Rue Auguste Lemaire, BP 6
F-92265 Fontenay-aux-Roses Cedex

Tel: +33 (1) 46 54 79 06
Fax: +33 (1) 46 54 72 90
E-mail: jean-claude.barescut@ipsn.fr

CALVEZ, Marianne
Commisariat a l'Energie Atomique (CEA)
Direction centrale de la securité
Service hygiène sécurité protection
Route du Panorama, BP 6
F-92265 Fontenay-aux-Roses Cedex

Tel: +33 01 46 54 92 48
Fax: +33 01 46 54 94 37
Eml: marianne.calvez@cea.fr

GALLERAND, Marie-Odile
ANDRA DS/BE
Parc de la Croix Blanc
1-7 rue Jean Monnet
F-92298 Chatenay Malabry

Tel: +33 1 46 11 80 41
Fax: +33 1 46 11 82 22
E-mail: mo.gallerand@andra.fr

JOUVE, André
Emergency Preparedness, Environment
Radiation Protection Dept.
Nuclear Installation Safety Directorate
BP 83, Route du Panorama Robert Schuman
F-92266 Fontenay-aux-Roses, Cedex

Tel: +33 (0)1 43 19 70 63
Fax: +33 (0)1 43 19 71 30
E-mail: Andre.JOUVE@asn.minefi.gouv.fr

METIVIER, Henri
2 allée des Hauts Futaies
F-91450 Soisy-sur-Seine

Tel: +33 01 69 89 98 81
Fax: +33 01 69 89 98 81
E-mail: henri.metivier@ipsn.fr

MONCHAUX, Georges
Institut de protection et
de sûreté nucléaire
BP6
92265 Fontenay-aux-Roses
Cedex

Tel: +33 (0) 1 46 54 70 48
Fax: +33 (0) 1 46 54 79 71
E-mail: georges.monchaux@ipsn.fr

SAINT-PIERRE, Sylvain
Manager
Radiation Protection Corporate
COGEMA, DSSQ
2, rue Paul Dautier, BP 4
F-78141 Vélizy Cedex

Tel: +33 1 39 26 38 71
Fax: +33 1 39 26 27 15
E-mail: ssaintpierre@cogema.fr

GERMANY

BECKER, Klaus
Radiation Science and Health
Boothstr.27,
D-12207 Berlin

Tel: +49 30 772 1284
Fax: +49 30 772 1284
E-mail: Prof.Dr.Klaus.Becker@t-online.de

STREFFER, Christian
Auf dem Sutan 12
D-45239 Essen

Tel: +49 201 49 26 16
Fax: +49 201 49 0 11 11
E-mail: streffer.essen@t-online.de

WIRTH, Erich
Institute for Atmospheric
Radioactivity
Federal Office for Radiation Protection
Rosastr. 9
D-79098 Freiburg

Tel: +49 761 386 6711
Fax: +49 761 382 459
E-mail: ewirth@bfs.de

ZAPPE, Dietmar
Gesellschaft für Anlagen -
und Reaktorsicherheit (GRS) mbh
Abteilung Endlagerung
Kurfürstendamm 200
D-10719 Berlin

E-mail: zad@grs.de

ICELAND

MAGNUSSON, Sigurdur M.
Director, Geislavarnir Rikisi
Icelandic Radiation Protection Institute
Raudararstigur 10
150 Reykjavik

Tel: +354 552 8200
Fax: +354 552 8202
E-mail: smm@gr.is

IRELAND

RAFFERTY, Barbara
Senior Scientific Officer
Radiological Protection Institute
3 Clonskeagh Sq.
Clonskeagh Road
Dublin 14

Tel: +353 1 269 7766
Fax: +353 1 269 7437
E-mail: brafferty@rpii.ie

ITALY

BATTISTONI, Palmira
ANPA NUC
Via Vitaliano Brancati n.48
I-00144 Roma

CUMO, Maurizio
Universita degli Studi di Roma
c/o ENEA
Viale Regina Margherita 125
I-00198 Roma

Tel: +39 06 6868 095
Fax: +39 06 6868 489
E-mail: maurizio.cumo@uiroma1.it

GALLINI, Rosina Manuela
Agenzia Regionale per la
Protezione dell'Ambiente
della Lombarida
Via Restellie 1
I-20124 Milano

Tel: +39 030 3838686
Fax: +39 030 394234
E-mail: fisica@aslbrescia.lombardia.it

MAGNONI, Mauro
ARPA Piemonte
Dip. Ivrea
Via Jervis 30
I-10015 Ivrea (To)

MAROTTA, Paolo
ARPA Campania
Via G. Porzio 4
Centro Direzionale Isola E5
I-80143 Napoli

MEZZANOTTE, Roberto
Director
Dept. Nuclear & Radiation Safety
ANPA
Via Vitaliano Brancati 48
I-00144 Rome

Tel: +39 06 5007 2254
Fax: +39 06 5007 2941
E-mail: mezzanotte@anpa.it

PICCOLI, Daniela
ANPA NUC
Via Vitaliano Brancati n.48
I-00144 Roma

RANIERI, Roberto
Head, Co-ordination of International
Activities
ANPA
Via Vitaliano Brancati 48
I-00144 Roma

Tel: +39 (06) 5007 2150
Fax: +39 (06) 5007 2941
E-mail: ranieri@anpa.it

RICCI, Renato Angelo
Commissario Straordinario ANPA
Via Vitaliano Brancati n.48,
I-00144 Roma

RISICA, Serena
Instituto Superiore di Sanità
Viale Regina Elena n.299
I-00161 Roma

SGRILLI, Enrico
Head, Inter-departmental Unit
Co-ordination of Inspections & Standards
ANPA
Via Vitaliano Brancati 48
I-00144 Roma

Tel: +39 06 50 07 28 50
Fax: +39 06 50 07 29 41
E-mail: sgrilli@anpa.it

TARRONI, Giuseppe
Head
Radiation Protection Institute
ENEA-PRO-IRP
Via dei Colli 16
I-40136 Bologna

Tel: +39 051 609 8344
Fax: +39 051 609 8003
Eml: tarroni@bologna.enea.it

TORRI, Giancarlo
ANPA
Via Vitaliano Brancati 48
I-00144 Roma

Tel: +39 06 50 07 20 41
Fax: +39 06 50 07 23 13
E-mail: torri@anpa.it

TOSI, Antonio
Coordinatore Comitato, DG
ARPA Campania
Via G. Porzio, 4
Centro Direzionale Isola E5
I-80143 Napoli

Tel: +39 081 778 2440
Fax: +39 081 778 2536

TRENTA, Giorgio
Via degli Archinto 4
I-00163 Roma

JAPAN

DOI, Masahiro
Head, Methodology Development
Environmental & Toxicological
Sciences Research Group (NIRS)
4-9-1 Anagawa, Inage,
Chiba 263-8555

Tel: +81 43 206 3150
Fax: +81 43 251 4853
E-mail: masa_doi@nirs.go.jp

FUJIMOTO, Kenzo
Director
Environmental Radiation
Protection Research Group (NIRS)
4-9-1 Anagawa, Inage-ku,
263-8555 Chiba

Tel: +81 43 206 3103
Fax: +81 43 284 1769
E-mail: kenzofuj@nirs.go.jp

KOSAKO, Toshiso
Research Center for Nuclear
Science & Technology
The University of Tokyo
Yayoi 2-11-16, Bunkyo-ku
Tokyo 113-0032

Tel: +81 3 58 41 29 22
Fax: +81 3 34 68 76 31
E-mail: kosako@rcnst.u-tokyo.ac.jp

MATSUBARA, Junko
Commissioner, Nuclear Safety Commission
Cabinet Office
3-1-1 Kasumigaseki, Chiyoda-ku
Tokyo 100-8970

Tel: +81 3 3581 3470
Fax: +81 3 3581 3475
E-mail: jmatsub@op.cao.go.jp

NETHERLANDS

CARROLL, Simon R.
Advisor, Political Unit
Greenpeace International
Kerersgracht 176
1016 DW Amsterdam

Tel: +31 20 523 6288
Fax: +31 20 523 6200
E-mail: scarroll@ams.greenpeace.org

O'SULLIVAN, Patrick J.
Nuclear Research & Consultancy Group
(NRG)
Postbus 25
1755 ZG Petten

Tel: +31 (0) 224 56 4533
Fax: +31 224 568491
E-mail: osullivan@nrg-nl.com

NORWAY

OUGHTON, Deborah
Norwegian Agricultural University
NLH
Postboks 5026
NO 1432 As

E-mail: Deborah.Oughton@ikb.nlh.no

SPAIN

CANCIO, David
CIEMAT
Depto de Impacto Ambiental
de la Energia
Avda. Complutense 22
28040 Madrid

Tel: +34 91 346 6628
Fax: +34 91 346 6121
Eml: david.cancio@ciemat.es

GIMENO, Carlos
Consejo de Seguridad Nuclear (CSN)
Justo Dorado, 11
28040 Madrid

Tel: +34 91 346 05 02
Fax: +34 91 346 03 93
E-mail: cgs@csn.es

GUTIERREZ LOPEZ, Jose
Director
Department of Environmental
Impact of Energy, CIEMAT
Avda. Complutense 22
28040 Madrid

Tel: +34 13 46 65 55
Fax: +34 13 46 61 21
E-mail: jose.gutierrez@ciemat.es

SALAS, Rosario
Head of Environmental Radiological
Monitoring Area
Nuclear Safety Council (CSN)
Justo Dorado, 11
28040 Madrid

Tel: +34 91 34 60 408
Fax: +34 91 34 60 497
E-mail: rsc@csn.es

SENDIN, Paloma
Counsellor
Consejo de Seguridad Nuclear (CSN)
Justo Dorado, 11
28040 Madrid

Tel: +34 (91) 346 0330
Fax: +34 (91) 346 0393
E-mail: psc@csn.es

SWEDEN

HOLM, Lars Erik
Swedish Radiation Protection Institute
S-171 16 Stockholm

Tel: +46 8 72 97 110
Fax: +46 8 72 97 108
E-mail: lars.erik.holm@ssi.se

LARSSON, Carl-Magnus
Dept. of Waste Management
and Environmental Protection
Swedish Radiation Protection Authority
SSI
S-171 16 Stockholm

Tel: +46 8 729 72 52
Fax: +46 8 729 71 08
E-mail: carl.magnus.larsson@ssi.se

SWITZERLAND

ANDRES, Roger
Division Hygiène des
Rayonnements
Institut Paul Scherrer
CH-5232 Villigen PSI

Tel: +41 (0)56 310 2347
Fax: +41 (0)56 310 2309
E-mail: roger.andres@psi.ch

UNITED KINGDOM

BACON, Michael L.
Health & Safety Executive
Nuclear Safety Directorate
Room 525, St Peter's House
Balliol Road, Bootle
Merseyside, L20 3LZ

Tel: +44 (0) 151 951 4099
Fax: +44 (0) 151 951 4100
E-mail: mick.bacon@hse.gsi.gov.uk

CLARKE, Roger H.
Director
National Radiological
Protection Board
Chilton, Didcot
Oxfordshire OX11 0RQ

Tel: +44 1235 82 26 32
Fax: +44 1235 82 26 19
E-mail: roger.clarke@nrpb.org.uk

FRY, Frances A.
National Radiological
Protection Board
Chilton, Didcot
Oxon OX11 ORQ

Tel: +44 (1235) 822618
Fax: +44 (1235) 822620
E-mail: frances.fry@nrpb.org

GIZE, Irene
Environment Agency
Knutsford Road
Warrington
WA4 1HG

Tel: +44 1925 653999
Fax: +44 1925 415961
E-mail: irene.gize@environment-agency.
gov.uk

JONES, Steve
Westlakes Research Institute
Westlakes Science Park
Moor Row
Cumbria CA24 3LN

Tel: +44 01946 514003
Fax: +44 01946 514033
E-mail: steve.jones@westlakes.ac.uk

MILLER, Andrew
Member of Parliament
House of Commons
London SW1A OAA

Tel: +44 207 219 3580
E-mail: millera@parliament.uk

PENTREATH, Jan
Environmental Systems
Science Centre
University of Reading
Whiteknights
Reading RG6 6A1

Tel: +44 118 931 4126
E-mail: Pentreath@supanet.com

UNITED STATES OF AMERICA

ABRAMS, Charlotte E.
Nuclear Regulatory Commission
(USNRC)
11545 Rockville Pike
Rockville, MD 20852 2738

Tel: +1 (301) 415 7293
Fax: +1 (301) 415 5397
E-mail: cea2@nrc.gov

ANDERSEN, Ralph
Chief Health Physicist
Nuclear Energy Institute
Suite 400
1776 Eye Street, NW
Washington, DC 20006-3708

Tel: +1 202 739 8111
Fax: +1 202 785 4019
E-mail: rla@nei.org

CLARK, Mary E.
Assistant Office Director, ORIA
Environmental Protection Agency
1200 Pennsylvania Avenue, N.W.
20460 Washington D.C.

Tel: +1 (202) 564 9348
Fax: +1 (202) 565 2043
E-mail: clark.marye@epa.gov

DICUS, Greta Joy
Commissioner
(Bldg OWFN, room 18 H1)
U.S. Nuclear Regulatory
Commission (NRC)
Washington, D.C. 20555

Tel: +1 (301) 415 1820
Fax: +1 (301) 415 3504
E-mail: cmrdicus@nrc.gov

DOMOTOR, Stephen L.
U.S. Department of Energy
(Environmental Policy and Guidance)
Room GA-098
1000 Independence Avenue, S.W.
Washington, DC 20585

Tel: +1 202 586 0871
Fax: +1 202 586 3915
E-mail: Stephen.Domotor@eh.doe.gov

JONES, C. Rick
Acting Deputy Assistant Secretary
for Safety and Health(EH-5)
U.S. Dept.of Energy
1000 Independence Avenue S.W.
Washington D.C.

Tel: +1 (202) 586 6539
Fax: +1 (202) 586 0956
E-mail: rick.jones@eh.doe.gov

JONES, Cynthia
Senior Advisor for Materials
Nuclear Regulatory Commission (NRC)
Mail Stop O16-C1
Washington, DC 20555-0001

Tel: +1 301-415-1829
Fax: +1 301-415-3504
E-mail: cgj@nrc.gov

TILL, John
President
Risk Assessment Corporation
417 Till Road
Neeses
South Carolina 29107

Tel: +1 803 536 4883
Fax: +1 803 534 1995
E-mail: johntill@mindspring.com

INTERNATIONAL ORGANISATIONS

GENTNER, Norman
UNSCEAR Scientific Secretary
Vienna International Centre
Room E0421
P.O. Box 500
A-1400 Vienna

Tel: +43 1 26060 4330
Fax: +43 1 26060 5902
E-mail: norman.gentner@unvienna.org

HUNTER, George
European Commission
Directorate General Environment C4
WAG C/243
Batiment Jean Monnet
L-2920 Luxembourg

Tel: +352 4301 36352
Fax: +352 4301 36280
E-mail: George.Hunter@cec.eu.int

LINSLEY, Gordon S.
Head, Waste Safety Section
Division of Radiation and Waste Safety
International Atomic Energy Agency
P.O.Box 100
A-1400 Vienne

Tel: +43 1 2600 22666
Fax: +43 1 26007
E-mail: g.linsley@iaea.org

ROBINSON, Carol
Waste Safety Section
Division of Radiation and Waste Safety
International Atomic Energy Agency
P.O. Box 100
A-1400 Vienna

Tel: +43 1 2600 22719
Fax: +43 1 26007
E-mail: C.Robinson@iaea.org

SCHULTE, Ernst
European Commission
DG RTD-J04 MO75 5/4
Nuclear Fission & Radiation Protection
200 rue de la Loi, Wetstraat
B-1049 Brussels

Tel: +32 2 295 7155
Fax: +32 2 295 4991
E-mail: ernst-hermann.schulte@cec.eu.int

SIMCOCK, Alan
Executive Secretary
OSPAR Secretariat
New Court
London WC2A 2JQ

Tel: +44 (0) 20 7430 5200
Fax: +44 (0) 20 7430 5225
E-mail: alan@ospar.org

VOIGT, Gabriele
IAEA
International Atomic Energy Agency
NAAL
Wagramerstr. 5
A-1400 Vienna

Tel: +43 1 2600 28224
Fax: +43 1 2600 28222
E-mail: g.voigt@iaea.org

CANCIO, David
IRPA Executive Board Member (Address see SPAIN)

NEA

SHIMOMURA, Kazuo
Deputy Director
OECD/Nuclear Energy Agency
Le Seine St-Germain
12 Boulevard des Iles
F-92130 Issy-les-Moulineaux

Tel: +33 01 45 24 10 04
Fax: +33 01 45 24 11 06
E-mail: kazuo.shimomura@oecd.org

RIOTTE, Hans
Head, Radiation Protection and
Waste Management Division
OECD Nuclear Energy Agency
12, boulevard des Iles
F-92130 Issy-les-Moulineaux

Tel: +33 (1) 45 24 10 40
Fax: +33 (1) 45 24 11 10
E-mail: hans.riotte@oecd.org

LAZO, Edward
Radiation Protection Division
OECD Nuclear Energy Agency
12, boulevard des Iles
Le Seine St. Germain
F-92130 Issy-les-Moulineaux

Tel: +33 (0)1 45 24 10 42
Fax: +33 (0)1 45 24 11 10
E-mail: edward.lazo@oecd.org

MUNDIGL, Stefan
Radiation Protection Division
OECD Nuclear Energy Agency
Le Seine St. Germain
12, boulevard des Iles
F-92130 Issy-les-Moulineaux

Tel: +33 01 45 24 10 45
Fax: +33 01 45 24 11 10
E-mail: mundigl@nea.fr

OECD PUBLICATION, 2, rue André-Pascal, 75775 PARIS CEDEX 16
PRINTED IN FRANCE
(66 2003 01 1 P) – No. 52829 2002